Revise
GCSE

Chemistry

Jon Dwyer and Emma Poole

S40

I0336915

Contents

4 Metals and tests

5 Acids, bases and salts

6 Calculation and physical chemistry

This book and

	AQA	Edexcel
Web Address	www.aqa.org.uk	www.edexcel.com
Specification Number	4402	2CH01
Exam Assessed Units and Modules At least 40% of assessment must be carried out at the end of the course. For students starting the GCSE course from September 2012 onwards, all assessment (100%) must take place at the end of the course.	**Unit 1: Chemistry 1** 1 hr 60 marks 25% of GCSE **Unit 2: Chemistry 2** 1 hr 60 marks 25% of GCSE **Unit 3: Chemistry 3** 1 hr 60 marks 25% of GCSE All papers feature structured and closed questions.	**Unit C1** 1 hr 60 marks 25% of GCSE **Unit C2** 1 hr 60 marks 25% of GCSE **Unit C3** 1 hr 60 marks 25% of GCSE All papers feature objective, short answer and extended writing questions.
Controlled Assessment Covering: · Research, planning and risk assessment · Data collection · Processing, analysis and evaluation	**Unit 4: Controlled Assessment** 1hr 35 min, plus time for research / data collection 50 marks 25% of GCSE	**Unit PCA** 3 hrs, plus preparation time 50 marks 25% of GCSE
Chapter Map*		
1 Atoms and materials	C1.1, C1.3, C1.5, C2.1, C2.2, C2.3, C2.6, C3.1	C1, C2, C3
2 The Earth and pollution	C1.2, C1.3, C1.4, C1.5, C1.7, C3.3	C1, C2, C3
3 Organic chemistry and analysis	C1.4, C1.5, C1.6, C2.2, C2.3, C3.6	C1, C2, C3
4 Metals and tests	C1.3, C2.1, C2.2, C2.7, C3.1, C3.3, C3.4	C1, C2, C3
5 Acids, bases and salts	C1.2, C2.6, C2.7, C3.2, C3.4	C1, C2, C3
6 Calculation and physical chemistry	C1.1, C1.5, C2.3, C2.4, C2.5, C3.3, C3.4, C3.5	C2, C3

* There are tick charts throughout the book to show which particular sub-topics in each chapter are relevant to your course.

your GCSE course

OCR A	OCR B	WJEC	CCEA
www.ocr.org.uk	www.ocr.org.uk	www.wjec.co.uk	www.ccea.org.uk
J244	J264	600/1035/6	G14
Modules C1, C2 and C3 1 hr 60 marks 25% of GCSE **Modules C4, C5 and C6** 1 hr 60 marks 25% of GCSE **Module C7** 1 hr 60 marks 25% of GCSE All papers feature objective style and free response questions.	**Modules C1, C2 and C3** 1 hr 15 min 75 marks 35% of GCSE **Modules C4, C5 and C6** 1 hr 30 min 85 marks 40% of GCSE Includes a data response section worth 10 marks, which assesses AO3 All papers feature structured questions.	**Chemistry 1** 1 hr 60 marks 25% of GCSE **Chemistry 2** 1 hr 60 marks 25% of GCSE **Chemistry 3** 1 hr 60 marks 25% of GCSE All papers feature structured questions involving some extended writing.	**Unit C1** Higher: 1 hr 30 min 100 marks Foundation: 1 hr 15 min 80 marks 35% of GCSE **Unit C2** Higher: 1 hr 45 min 115 marks Foundation: 1 hr 30 min 90 marks 40% of GCSE All papers feature structured questions.
Unit A174 Approx. 4.5–6 hrs 64 marks 25% of GCSE	**Unit B743** Approx. 7 hrs 48 marks 25% of GCSE	**Unit CA** Approx. 7.5 hrs, plus time for initial research 48 marks 25% of GCSE	**Unit 3** 1 hr, plus time for planning, risk assessment and data collection 45 marks 25% of GCSE
C2, C4, C5, C6, C7	C1, C2, C3, C4, C5, C6	C1, C2	C1, C2
C1, C2, C3, C5, C7	C1, C2, C6	C1, C2, C3	C1, C2
C1, C2, C7	C1, C3, C6	C1, C2, C3	C1, C2
C1, C3, C4, C5, C6, C7	C1, C2, C3, C4, C5, C6	C1, C2, C3	C1, C2
C3, C4, C5, C6, C7	C1, C2, C4, C5, C6	C1, C2, C3	C1, C2
C5, C6, C7	C2, C3, C5, C6	C2, C3	C1, C2

5

Preparing for the exams

What will be assessed

In your science exams and controlled assessment you are assessed on three main criteria called assessment objectives:

- **Assessment Objective 1 (AO1)** – tests your ability to **recall**, select and communicate your knowledge and understanding of chemistry
- **Assessment Objective 2 (AO2)** – tests your ability to **apply** your skills, knowledge and understanding of chemistry in practical and other contexts
- **Assessment Objective 3 (AO3)** – tests your ability to **analyse** and **evaluate** evidence, make reasoned judgements and draw conclusions based on evidence

The exam papers have a lot of AO1 and AO2 questions and some AO3 questions. The controlled assessments focus mainly on AO2 and AO3.

To do well on the exams, it is not enough just to be able to recall facts. You must be able to apply your knowledge to different scenarios, analyse and evaluate evidence and formulate your own ideas and conclusions.

Planning your study

It is important to have an organised approach to study and revision throughout the course.

- After completing a topic in school or college, go through the topic again using this guide. Copy out the main points on a piece of paper or use a pen to highlight them.
- Much of memory is visual. Make sure your notes are laid out in a logical way using colour, charts, diagrams and symbols to present information in a visual way. If your notes are easy to read and attractive to the eye, they will be easier to remember.
- A couple of days, later try writing out the key points from memory. Check differences between what you wrote originally and what you wrote later.
- If you have written your notes on a piece of paper, make sure you keep them for revision later.
- Try some questions in the book and check your answers.
- Decide whether you have fully mastered the topic and write down any weaknesses you think you have.

How this book will help you

This complete study and revision guide will help you because...

- it contains the essential content for your GCSE course without the extra material that will not be examined.
- there are regular short progress checks so that you can test your understanding.
- it contains Sample GCSE questions with model answers and notes, so that you can see what the examiner is looking for.
- it contains Exam practice questions so that you can confirm your understanding and practise answering exam-style questions.
- the summary table on pages 4–5, and the exam-board signposting throughout the book, will ensure that only study and revise topics that are relevant to your course.

Six ways to improve your grade

1. Read the question carefully

Many students fail to answer the actual question set. Perhaps they misread the question or answer a similar question that they have seen before. Read the question once right through and then again more slowly. Underline key words in the question as you read through it. Questions at GCSE often contain a lot of information. You should be concerned if you are not using the information in your answer.

Take notice of the command words used in questions and make sure you answer appropriately:

- **State:** A concise, factual answer with no description or explanation
- **Describe:** A detailed answer that demonstrates knowledge of the facts about the topic
- **Explain:** A more detailed answer than a description; give reasons and use connectives like 'because'.
- **Calculate:** Give a numerical answer, including working and correct units
- **Suggest:** A personal response supported by facts.

2. Give enough detail

If a part of a question is worth three marks, you should make at least three separate points. Be careful that you do not make the same point three times, but worded in a slightly different way. Draw diagrams with a ruler and label with straight lines.

3. Be specific

Avoid using the word 'it' in your answers. Writing out in full what you are referring to will ensure the examiner knows what you are talking about. This is especially important in questions where you have to compare two or more things.

4. Use scientific language correctly

Try to use the correct scientific language in your answers. The way scientific language is used is often the difference between successful and unsuccessful students. As you revise, make a list of scientific terms you come across and check that you understand what they mean. Learn all the definitions. These are easy marks and they reward effort and good preparation.

5. Show your working

All science papers include calculations. Learn a set method for solving a calculation and use that method. You should always show your working in full. That way, if you make an arithmetical mistake, you may still receive marks for applying the correct science. Check your answer is given to the correct level of accuracy (significant figures or decimal places) and give the correct units.

6. Brush up on your writing skills

Your exam papers will include specific questions for which the answers will be marked on both scientific accuracy and the quality of the written communication. These questions are worth 6 marks, but it does not matter how good the science is, your answer will not gain full marks unless:

- the text is legible and the spelling, punctuation and grammar are accurate so that your meaning is clear
- you have used a form and style of writing that is fit for purpose and appropriate to the subject matter
- you have organised information in a clear and logical way, correctly using scientific vocabulary where appropriate.

These questions will be clearly indicated on the exam papers.

> Exam papers are scanned and marked on a computer screen. Do not write outside the answer spaces allowed, or your work may not be seen by the examiner. Ask for extra paper if you need it. Choose a black pen that will show up – one that photocopies well is a good choice.

How Science Works

The science GCSE courses are designed to help develop your knowledge of certain factual details, but also your understanding of 'How Science Works'.

'How Science Works' is essentially a set of key concepts that are relevant to all areas of science. It is concerned with four main areas:

Data, evidence, theories and explanations

- science as an evidence-based discipline
- the collaborative nature of science as a discipline and the way new scientific knowledge is validated
- how scientific understanding and theories develop
- the limitations of science
- how and why decisions about science and technology are made
- the use of modelling, including mathematical modelling, to explain aspects of science

Practical skills

- developing hypotheses
- planning practical ways to test hypotheses
- the importance of working accurately and safely
- identifying hazards and assessing risks
- collecting, processing, analysing and interpreting primary and secondary data
- reviewing methodology to assess fitness for purpose
- reviewing hypotheses in light of outcomes

Communication skills

- communicating scientific information using scientific, technical and mathematical language, conventions, and symbols.
- use models to explain systems, processes and abstract ideas

Applications and implications of science

- the ethical implications of chemistry and its applications
- risk factors and risk assessment in the context of potential benefit

You will be taught about 'How Science Works' throughout the course in combination with the scientific content. Likewise, the different exam boards have included material about 'How Science Works' in different parts of their assessment.

'How Science Works' will be assessed in the controlled assessment, but you will also get questions that relate to it in the exams. If you come across questions about unfamiliar situations in the exam, do not panic and think that you have not learnt the work. Most of these questions are designed to test your skills and understanding of 'How Science Works', not your memory. The examiners want you to demonstrate what you know, understand and can do.

1 Atoms and materials

The following topics are covered in this chapter:

- Atomic structure
- Atoms and the periodic table
- Chemical reactions and atoms
- The periodic table
- Balancing equations
- Ionic and covalent bonding
- Ionic and covalent structures
- Group 7
- New materials
- Synthesis

1.1 Atomic structure

LEARNING SUMMARY

After studying this section, you should be able to:

- Name the three types of particle present in an atom.
- Describe the three types of particle in terms of mass, charge and where found.
- Use the atomic number and mass number to work out how many of each type of particle is present.
- Work out the electron arrangement for an atom of a given element.
- Describe the difference between isotopes of the same element.

Elements

AQA	C1	✓
OCR A	C4	✓
EDEXCEL	C2	✓
WJEC	C1, C2	✓
CCEA	C1	✓

KEY POINT

A substance that is made of only one type of **atom** is called an **element**.

Elements cannot be broken down chemically. Atoms of different elements have different properties. About 100 different elements have been discovered. The elements can be represented by **symbols**.

Approximately 80% of the elements are **metals**. Metals are found on the left-hand side and in the centre of the periodic table. The **non-metal** elements are found on the right-hand side of the periodic table. Elements with **intermediate properties** such as germanium are found in group 4.

Structure of the atom

AQA	C1, C2	✓
OCR A	C4	✓
OCR B	C4	✓
EDEXCEL	C1, C2	✓
WJEC	C1, C2	✓
CCEA	C1	✓

An atom has a very small, central **nucleus** that is surrounded by shells of **electrons**. The nucleus is found at the centre of the atom. It contains **protons** and **neutrons**.

- Protons have a mass of 1 **atomic mass unit (amu)** and a charge of 1+.
- Neutrons also have a mass of 1 amu but no charge.
- Electrons have a negligible mass and a charge of 1−.

Structure of an atom

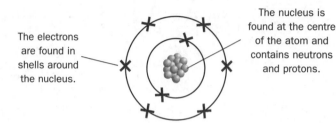

The electrons are found in shells around the nucleus.

The nucleus is found at the centre of the atom and contains neutrons and protons.

> Atoms are very small. They have a radius of about 10^{-10} m and a mass of about 10^{-23} g.

All atoms are **neutral**: there is no overall charge, so the number of protons must be equal to the number of electrons.

You may have seen two numbers written next to an element's symbol. These numbers are the **mass number** and the **atomic number**. They provide information about the particles inside the atom.

Mass number and atomic number

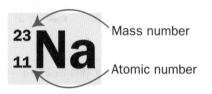

$^{23}_{11}\text{Na}$ Mass number / Atomic number

The mass number is the number of protons added to the number of neutrons. The atomic number is the number of protons (so it is also known as the **proton number**). All the atoms of a particular element have the same number of protons, for example, carbon atoms always have six protons. Atoms of different elements have different atomic numbers.

> Be familiar with the mass and charge of the three types of particle found inside an atom. All atoms of the same element have the same number of protons and electrons. For example, all atoms of oxygen contain 8 protons and 8 electrons.

Sodium has an atomic number of 11, so every sodium atom has 11 protons. A sodium atom has no overall charge, so the number of electrons must be the same as the number of protons. Sodium atoms therefore have 11 electrons. The number of neutrons is given by the mass number minus the atomic number. In sodium that is 23 − 11 = 12 neutrons.

Electron structure

AQA	C1	✓
OCR A	C4	✓
OCR B	C4	✓
EDEXCEL	C2	✓
WJEC	C2	✓
CCEA	C1	✓

Electrons occupy the lowest available **shell** (or energy level). This is the shell that is closest to the nucleus. When this is full the electrons start to fill the next shell. In the diagram, the first shell may contain up to two electrons while the second and third shells may contain up to eight electrons.

A model of electron shells

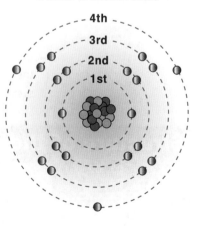

4th
3rd
2nd
1st

KEY POINT

The electron structure of an atom is important because it determines how the atom (and, therefore, the element) will react.

Groups

AQA	C1, C3	✓
OCR A	C4	✓
OCR B	C4	✓
EDEXCEL	C2	✓
WJEC	C1, C2	✓
CCEA	C1	✓

KEY POINT

Elements in the same **group** (the same vertical column) of the periodic table have similar chemical properties because they have the same number of electrons in their outer shells.

Element	Number of protons	Number of electrons	Electronic structure	Number of shells of electrons	Group of periodic table	Period of periodic table	Diagram
Lithium	3	3	2, 1	2	1	2	
Magnesium	12	12	2, 8, 2	3	2	3	

Across a **period** (the same horizontal row in the periodic table), each consecutive element has one extra proton in its nucleus and one extra electron in its outer shell of electrons. This means an electron shell is filled with electrons across a period.

Isotopes

AQA	C2	✓
OCR B	C4	✓
EDEXCEL	C2	✓
WJEC	C2	✓
CCEA	C1	✓

Isotopes of an element have the same number of protons but a different number of neutrons. So, they have the same **atomic number** (that is, number of protons) but a different **mass number** (that is, number of protons and neutrons added together).

Chlorine has two isotopes:

Isotope	Protons	Electrons	Neutrons	Diagram
Chlorine–35	17	17	18	$^{35}_{17}\text{Cl}$
Chlorine–37	17	17	20	$^{37}_{17}\text{Cl}$

These isotopes will have slightly different physical properties but will **react identically** in chemical reactions because they have identical numbers of electrons.

> Learn the definition for relative atomic mass.

The relative atomic mass of an element compares the mass of atoms of the element with the carbon-12 isotope. The existence of isotopes means that some elements have relative atomic masses that are not a whole number, for example, chlorine has a relative atomic mass of 35.5.

25% of chlorine atoms have an atomic mass of 37.

75% of chlorine atoms have an atomic mass of 35.

This gives an average atomic mass of 35.5.

PROGRESS CHECK

1. What does the nucleus of an atom contain?
2. Which particles are found in shells around the nucleus?
3. What is the charge and mass of a proton?
4. What is the charge and mass of an electron?
5. What is the charge and mass of a neutron?
6. What is the mass number of an atom?
7. Calcium and magnesium both belong to group 2 of the periodic table. Why does the element calcium react in a similar way to the element magnesium?

7. As both elements are in group 2 of the periodic table they have a similar electron configuration; they both have two electrons in their outer shell.
6. The number of protons plus the number of neutrons.
5. No charge, mass 1 amu.
4. Charge −1, mass negligible.
3. Charge +1, mass 1 amu.
2. Electrons.
1. Protons and neutrons.

1.2 Atoms and the periodic table

LEARNING SUMMARY

After studying this section, you should be able to:

- Describe how our understanding of atoms has changed, over time.
- Link the names of scientists to important theories about atoms.
- Describe the experiment that led Rutherford to propose the existence of a dense nucleus.
- Describe the arrangement of elements on the modern periodic table as being according to atomic number.
- Relate the group and period number of a given element to its electron arrangement.

The history of the atom

AQA	C3	✓
OCR A	C4	✓
OCR B	C4	✓
WJEC	C1, C2	✓
CCEA	C1	✓

Ideas about atoms have changed over time as more evidence has become available. Scientists look at the evidence that is available and use this to build a model of what they think is happening. As new evidence emerges they re-evaluate the model. If the model fits with the new evidence they keep it. If the model no longer works they change it.

Important advances

OCR A	C4	✓
OCR B	C4	✓
WJEC	C2	✓
CCEA	C1	✓

John Dalton

In the early 1800s, John Dalton developed a theory about atoms, which included these predictions:

- Elements are made up of small particles called atoms.
- Atoms cannot be divided into simpler substances.
- All atoms of the same element are the same.
- Atoms of each element are different from atoms of other elements.

JJ Thomson

Between 1897 and 1906 Thomson discovered that atoms could be split into smaller particles. He discovered electrons and found that they:

- have a negative charge
- are very small
- are deflected by magnetic and electric fields.

He thought that atoms consisted of tiny negative electrons surrounded by a 'sea' of positive charge. Overall, the atom was neutral. This was called the **plum-pudding** theory of atoms.

JJ Thomson's 'plum-pudding' model of the atom

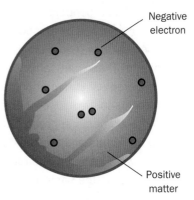

Negative electron

Positive matter

Ernest Rutherford

In 1909, Rutherford examined the results of Geiger and Marsden's experiment in which they had bombarded a very thin sheet of gold with alpha particles. The scientists recorded the pathway of the alpha particles through the gold leaf. To

Rutherford's amazement, he found that while most alpha particles (which are positively charged) passed through the gold atoms undeflected, a small number of alpha particles were deflected a little, and a tiny number of particles were deflected back towards the source. From his observations, Rutherford concluded that the positive charge in the atom must be concentrated in a very small area of the atom. This area is the nucleus of the atom.

The Geiger–Marsden experiment helped Rutherford to devise his 'nuclear' model of the atom

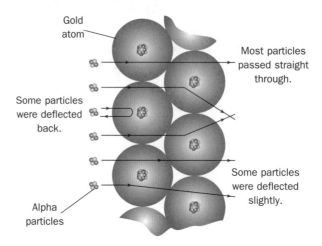

Gold atom

Most particles passed straight through.

Some particles were deflected back.

Some particles were deflected slightly.

Alpha particles

> Try designing a timeline to show how ideas about atoms have evolved over time. Include a section for each of the scientists above.

Neils Bohr

In 1913, Neils Bohr deduced that electrons must be found in certain areas in the atom otherwise they would spiral in towards the nucleus.

The modern periodic table

AQA	C3	✓
OCR A	C4	✓
OCR B	C4	✓
EDEXCEL	C2	✓
WJEC	C1	✓
CCEA	C1	✓

KEY POINT

In the modern periodic table, elements are arranged in order of increasing atomic number.

> All the isotopes of an element have the same number of electrons and protons. All the isotopes of an element appear in the same place on the periodic table.

It is called a periodic table because elements with similar properties occur at regular intervals or 'periodically'. The elements are placed in horizontal rows, called **periods**, and elements with similar properties appear in the same vertical column. These vertical columns are called **groups**. The groups may sometimes be numbered using roman numerals, so 'group 3' may be written as 'group III'. The elements in group 1 of the periodic table include lithium, sodium and potassium. All the elements in group 1 of the periodic table share similar properties: they are all metals and they all consist of atoms that have just one electron in their outer shell. When these metals react they form **ions**, which have a 1+ charge. Elements in the same period have the same number of shells of electrons.

PROGRESS CHECK

1. Why do scientists have to re-evaluate existing models?
2. How are the elements arranged in the modern periodic table?
3. What are the horizontal rows in the periodic table called?
4. What are the vertical columns in the periodic table called?
5. John Dalton made a number of predictions about atoms. Today, which of his predictions is not thought to be correct? Explain your answer.

PROGRESS CHECK

different number of neutrons.
are different forms of the same element that have the same number of protons and a
All atoms of the same element are the same. Scientists now know about isotopes. These
that atoms are made of protons, neutrons and electrons.
5. Dalton predicted that atoms cannot be divided into simpler substances. It is now known
4. Groups.
3. Periods.
2. They are in order of increasing atomic number.
1. To check them against new available evidence.

1.3 Chemical reactions and atoms

After studying this section, you should be able to:

LEARNING SUMMARY

- Use symbols to represent the chemical elements.
- Use formulae to represent chemical compounds.
- Interpret a chemical formula in terms of the type and ratio of the atoms that have combined.
- Recall the two different ways atoms can bond together to form compounds.
- Work out the formula of an ionic compound from the electrical charges of the ions.

Symbols

AQA	C1	✓
OCR B	C1–C4	✓
EDEXCEL	C1–C3	✓
CCEA	C1	✓

In science, elements can be represented by **symbols**. Each element has its own unique symbol that is recognised all over the world. Each symbol consists of one or two letters and is much easier to read and write than the full name. In some cases the symbol for an element is simply the first letter of the element's name. This letter must be a capital letter. The element iodine is represented by the symbol I.

Occasionally an element may take its symbol from its former Latin name. When this happens, the first letter is a capital and the second letter, if there is one, is lower case. The element mercury is represented by the symbol Hg. This comes from the Latin name for mercury, which was *hydrargyrum,* or **liquid silver**.

Remember to use your periodic table to check any symbols you are using. Don't forget that if a symbol has two letters, the first letter is a capital and the second is lower case.

Several elements have names that start with the same letter. When this happens, the first letter of the element's name is used, together with another letter from the name. The first letter is a capital and the second letter is lower case. The element magnesium is represented by the symbol Mg. The element manganese is represented by the symbol Mn.

Chemical formulae

AQA	C1	✓
OCR A	C2	✓
OCR B	C1–C6	✓
EDEXCEL	C1–C3	✓
WJEC	C1, C2	✓
CCEA	C1	✓

> **KEY POINT**
>
> A **compound** can be represented using a chemical **formula**. The formula shows the type and ratio of the atoms that are joined together in the compound.

A model of ammonia

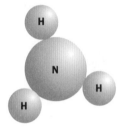

Ammonia has the chemical formula NH_3. This shows that in ammonia, nitrogen and hydrogen atoms are joined together in the ratio of one nitrogen atom to three hydrogen atoms.

You should take care when writing out the symbols for chemical compounds as some of them are very similar to elements. For example:

- The element carbon has the symbol C.
- The element oxygen has the symbol O.
- The element cobalt has the symbol Co.

> Take care when writing formulae with subscript numbers. They will need to be perfect to get the mark awarded in the exam.

The formula CO shows that a carbon atom and an oxygen atom have been chemically combined in a 1 : 1 ratio. This is the formula of the compound carbon monoxide. The symbol Co represents the element cobalt. Notice how the second letter of the symbol is written in lower case. If it wasn't, it would be a completely different substance. The formula CO_2 shows that carbon and oxygen atoms have been chemically combined in a 1 : 2 ratio. This is the formula of the compound carbon dioxide.

Chemical reactions

AQA	C1, C2	✓
OCR A	C2	✓
OCR B	C1–C6	✓
EDEXCEL	C2	✓
WJEC	C1, C2	✓
CCEA	C1	✓

An atom

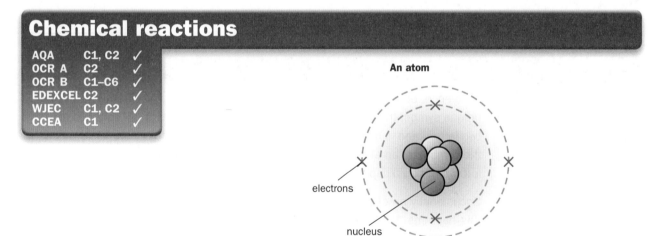

electrons

nucleus

Atoms of different elements can join together by forming new chemical **bonds**.

> **KEY POINT**
>
> Atoms can join together by:
>
> - **covalent bonding** – sharing electrons
> - **ionic bonding** – transferring electrons.

Compounds consist of two or more different types of atom that have been chemically combined. Compounds formed from metals and non-metals consist of ions. These compounds are held together by strong electrostatic forces of attraction. Compounds formed from non-metals consist of molecules. Giant molecules are held together by strong **covalent** bonds.

Word and symbol equations

AQA	C1	✓
OCR A	C4	✓
OCR B	C1–C6	✓
EDEXCEL	C1–C3	✓
WJEC	C1, C2	✓
CCEA	C1	✓

Symbol equations can be used to explain what happens during a chemical reaction. When magnesium burns in air the magnesium metal reacts with the non-metal atoms in oxygen molecules to form the **ionic** compound magnesium oxide. This reaction can be shown in a word equation:

magnesium + oxygen $\rightarrow$ magnesium oxide

or by the symbol equation:

$$2Mg + O_2 \rightarrow 2MgO$$

When carbon reacts with oxygen the non-metal carbon atoms react with the non-metal oxygen atoms to form molecules of the covalent compound carbon dioxide. This reaction can be shown in a word equation:

carbon + oxygen $\rightarrow$ carbon dioxide

or by the symbol equation:

$$C + O_2 \rightarrow CO_2$$

KEY POINT

Atoms are not created or destroyed during a chemical reaction: the atoms are just rearranged. This means that the total mass of the **reactants** is the same as the total mass of the **products**.

Ionic compounds

AQA	C2, C3	✓
OCR B	C4	✓
EDEXCEL	C2, C3	✓
WJEC	C1, C2	✓

Ionic compounds are formed when a metal reacts with a non-metal. When metal atoms react they lose negatively charged electrons to become positively charged ions (or **cations**). While when non-metal atoms react they gain negatively charged electrons to become negatively charged ions (or **anions**).

There is no overall charge for the ionic compounds so you can use the charge on the ions to work out the formula of the ionic compound.

Metal ions	Non-metal ions
Sodium, Na^+	Bromide, Br^-
Potassium, K^+	Chloride, Cl^-

The compound sodium chloride contains sodium, Na^+, and chloride, Cl^-, ions. For every one sodium ion one chloride ion is required. The overall formula for the compound is NaCl. The compound potassium bromide contains potassium, K^+, and bromide, Br^-, ions. For every one potassium ion one bromide ion is required. The overall formula for the compound is KBr.

PROGRESS CHECK

1. How can atoms join together?
2. Give the name of the element with the symbol Na.
3. Give the name of the element with the symbol Cr.
4. A water molecule has the formula H_2O. Explain what this formula tells us.

PROGRESS CHECK

⑤ Sodium nitrate has the formula $NaNO_3$. Explain what this formula tells us.

⑥ Give the formula for the following compounds:

a) Potassium chloride.

b) Sodium bromide.

6. a) KCl.
   b) NaBr.
5. It consists of sodium atoms, nitrogen atoms and oxygen atoms in the ratio 1 : 1 : 3.
4. It consists of 2 hydrogen atoms and 1 oxygen atom.
3. Chromium.
2. Sodium.
1. Atoms can be joined by sharing electrons or by transferring electrons.

1.4 The periodic table

LEARNING SUMMARY

After studying this section, you should be able to:

- Recall that Dobereiner's triads and Newlands' octaves were early attempts to show patterns in the properties of elements.
- Understand the reasoning behind Mendeleev's arrangement of the elements.
- Recognise the strengths and weaknesses of Mendeleev's Periodic Table.
- Understand the significance of groups and periods in relation to electron arrangements.
- Recall some of the properties of the transition elements.

Early ideas

OCR A	C4	✓
OCR B	C4	✓
EDEXCEL	C2	✓
CCEA	C1	✓

As new **elements** were discovered, scientists struggled to find links between them. In 1829, the German chemist Johann Wolfgang Dobereiner noticed that many elements could be put into groups of three, which he called **triads**. If these elements were placed in order of **atomic weight**, the atomic weight of the middle element was about the average of the lighter and the heavier elements. He noticed a similar pattern when he compared the densities of the members of a triad. Unfortunately, this pattern only appeared to work for some groups of elements.

Key developments

AQA	C3	✓
OCR A	C4	✓
OCR B	C4	✓
EDEXCEL	C2	✓
CCEA	C1	✓

In 1863, the English chemist John Newlands, noticed that if the known elements were placed in order of their atomic weight, and then put into rows of seven, there were strong similarities between elements in the same vertical column i.e. each element was similar to the one eight places on. This pattern became known as **Newlands' law of octaves**. It was useful for some of the elements but unfortunately Newlands' pattern broke down when he tried to include the **transition elements**.

Newlands

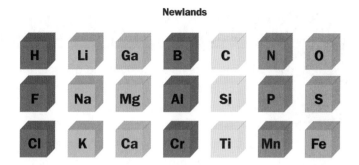

The **noble gases** are not shown in the diagram. They were only discovered in the 1890s when chemists noticed that the density of nitrogen made in reactions was slightly different from the density of nitrogen obtained directly from the air. The chemists thought the air might contain small amounts of other gases and so they devised experiments that eventually confirmed the presence of the very **unreactive** noble gases. They found that the air includes nitrogen, oxygen, neon and argon.

Mendeleev's idea

AQA	C3	✓
OCR A	C4	✓
OCR B	C4	✓
EDEXCEL	C2	✓
WJEC	C1	✓
CCEA	C1	✓

In 1869, the Russian chemist Dimitri **Mendeleev** produced his periodic table of elements. In his table, elements with similar properties occurred periodically and were placed in vertical columns called **groups**. Like Newlands, Mendeleev arranged the elements in order of increasing atomic weight, but unlike Newlands he did not stick strictly to this order.

> **KEY POINT**
>
> He left gaps for elements that had yet to be discovered, such as germanium and gallium, and made detailed predictions about the physical and chemical **properties** these elements would have.

> Mendeleev was not aware of protons, neutrons or electrons as they were not discovered until much later. Make sure you do not say he knew about them when you are answering exam questions.

Eventually, when these elements were discovered and their properties analysed, scientists were impressed by the accuracy of Mendeleev's predictions. Mendeleev's table went from being an interesting curiosity to a useful tool for understanding how a particular element would behave. Mendeleev would sometimes swap the order of the elements if their properties suggested it would be right to do so.

Atomic number

AQA	C1–C3	✓
OCR A	C4	✓
OCR B	C4	✓
EDEXCEL	C2	✓
WJEC	C2	✓
CCEA	C1	✓

By leaving gaps and swapping the order of the elements, Mendeleev had actually arranged the elements in order of **increasing atomic number** (or number of protons in the nucleus of an atom), even though protons themselves were not discovered until much later. In fact, electrons, protons and neutrons were all discovered in the early 20th century.

The modern periodic table

AQA	C1, C3 ✓
OCR B	C4 ✓
EDEXCEL	C2 ✓
WJEC	C1 ✓
CCEA	C1 ✓

The modern periodic table is arranged in order of increasing atomic number. You must make this clear in your answers. Many students refer to increasing mass number, which is not correct.

Today, scientists consider the periodic table an important summary of the structure of atoms. The elements in the modern periodic table are arranged in order of increasing atomic number. The group that the element belongs to is the same as the number of electrons that each atom of that element has in its outermost shell. Magnesium is in group 2 of the periodic table, so an atom of magnesium has two electrons in its outermost shell. Oxygen is in group 6 of the periodic table, so an atom of oxygen has six electrons in its outermost shell. The noble gases have a full outermost shell of electrons and no electrons at all in the next shell, so they all belong to group 0. The vertical rows are called periods. The period the element belongs to indicates the number of shells that are occupied by electrons for an atom of that element. A detailed periodic table can be used to find the names, symbols, relative atomic masses and atomic number of any element.

Transition metals

AQA	C1, C3 ✓
OCR B	C4 ✓
EDEXCEL	C2 ✓
WJEC	C1 ✓
CCEA	C1 ✓

The transition metals are found in the central block of the periodic table. The transition metals are much less reactive than group 1 metals. Transition metals have high melting points so, with the exception of mercury, are solid at room temperature. They are hard and strong and make useful structural materials. They do not react with water or oxygen as vigorously as group 1 metals, although many will show signs of corrosion over long periods of time.

Transition metal ions

AQA	C1, C3 ✓
OCR B	C1, C4 ✓

When transition metals form compounds the transition metal ions have **variable charges**. For example, in copper(II) oxide, CuO, the copper ions have a 2+ charge, while in copper(I) oxide, Cu_2O, the copper ions have a 1+ charge. The roman numerals given in the name of the transition metal compound shows the charge on the transition metal ion. Transition metal compounds are coloured; group 1 and 2 metal compounds are white. Transition metals and transition metal compounds are useful catalysts (chemicals that speed up chemical reactions). Iron is used in the Haber process (which produces ammonia) while nickel is used in the hydrogenation of ethene.

PROGRESS CHECK

1. What is the name given to Mendeleev's way of arranging the elements?
2. Why did Mendeleev not include the element germanium in his arrangement of the elements?
3. What group does magnesium belong to?
4. What group does oxygen belong to?
5. What is the charge on the copper ion in the compound copper(II) oxide?

PROGRESS CHECK

1. The periodic table.
2. It had not been discovered.
3. Group 2.
4. Group 6.
5. 2+.

1.5 Balancing equations

LEARNING SUMMARY

After studying this section, you should be able to:

- Recall that mass is always conserved in chemical reactions.
- Understand the advantage of using a symbol equation over a word equation.
- Decide if an equation is balanced, by counting atoms on both sides.
- Balance an equation that is not balanced, by adding numbers in front of symbols.
- Understand the use of state symbols in a chemical equation.

Conservation of mass

AQA	C1	✓
OCR A	C6	✓
OCR B	C1–C5	✓
EDEXCEL	C1–C3	✓
WJEC	C1	✓
CCEA	C1	✓

Symbol equations show the type and ratio of the atoms involved in a reaction. The **reactants** are placed on the left-hand side of the equation. The **products** are placed on the right-hand side of the equation. Overall, mass is **conserved** because atoms are never made or destroyed during chemical reactions. This means that there must always be the same number of each type of atom on both sides of the equation.

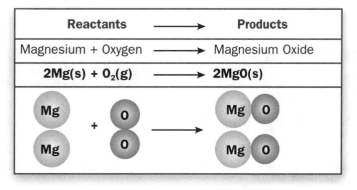

Reactants	⟶	Products
Magnesium + Oxygen	⟶	Magnesium Oxide
$2Mg(s) + O_2(g)$	⟶	$2MgO(s)$

Balancing the equation

AQA	C1	✓
OCR A	C4–C6	✓
OCR B	C1–C5	✓
EDEXCEL	C1–C3	✓
WJEC	C1	✓
CCEA	C1	✓

Hydrogen burns in air to produce water vapour. This can be shown using a word equation.

Hydrogen + Oxygen → Water

The word equation is useful but it doesn't give the ratio of hydrogen and oxygen molecules involved. Balanced symbol equations show this extra information. First, replace the words with symbols. Hydrogen and oxygen both exist as molecules.

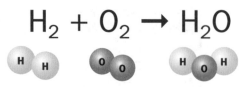

$$H_2 + O_2 \rightarrow H_2O$$

The formulae are all correct, but the equation does not balance because there are different numbers of atoms on each side of the equation. The formulae cannot be changed, but numbers can be added in front of the formulae to balance the equation.

The equation shows that there are two oxygen atoms on the left-hand side of the equation but only one oxygen atom on the right-hand side.

A number 2 is therefore placed in front of the H_2O:

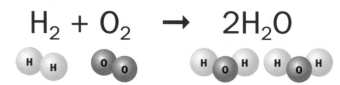

$$H_2 + O_2 \rightarrow 2H_2O$$

Now the oxygen atoms are balanced: there is the same number of oxygen atoms on both sides of the equation. However, the hydrogen atoms are no longer balanced. There are two hydrogen atoms on the left-hand side and four hydrogen atoms on the right-hand side. So a 2 is placed in front of the H_2:

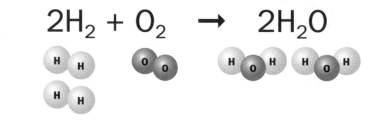

$$2H_2 + O_2 \rightarrow 2H_2O$$

The equation is now balanced.

> To get a top mark, you need to be able to balance equations. This skill just needs a little practice. Deal with each type of atom in turn until everything balances.
>
> Remember to write any subscripts below the line:
>
> H_2O is correct while H^2O and H2O are wrong.

State symbols

AQA	C2	✓
OCR A	C4–C6	✓
OCR B	C5	✓
EDEXCEL	C1–C3	✓
WJEC	C1	✓
CCEA	C1	✓

State symbols can be added to an equation to show extra information. They show what physical state the reactants and products are in. The symbols are:

- (s) for solid
- (l) for liquid
- (g) for gases
- (aq) for aqueous, or dissolved in water.

> Aqueous comes from the Latin *aqua* meaning water. Aqueous means dissolved in water.

Magnesium metal can be burned in air to produce magnesium oxide. Magnesium and magnesium oxide are both solids. The part of the air that reacts when things are burned is oxygen, which is a gas.

magnesium + oxygen → magnesium oxide

2Mg(s) + O$_2$(g) → 2MgO(s)

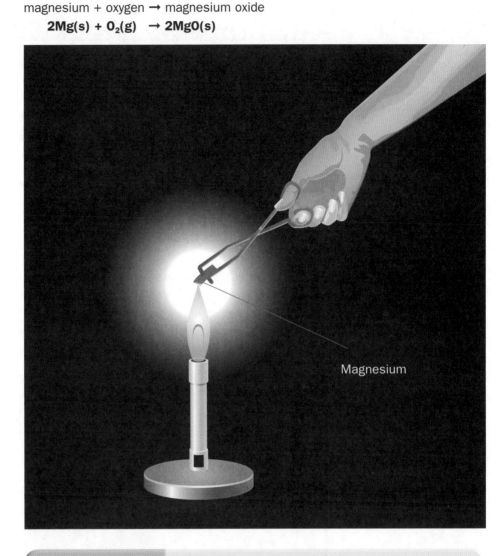

Magnesium

KEY POINT

When balancing equations, always check that the formulae you have written down are correct.

Some equations involve formulae that contain brackets, for example, calcium hydroxide: Ca(OH)$_2$. This means that calcium hydroxide contains calcium, oxygen and hydrogen atoms in the ratio 1 : 2 : 2. These equations can be balanced normally. Calcium reacts with water to form calcium hydroxide, which is slightly soluble, and hydrogen gas.

calcium + water → calcium hydroxide + hydrogen

Ca(s) + 2H$_2$O(l) → Ca(OH)$_2$(aq) + H$_2$(g)

Precipitation reactions

AQA	C1, C2	✓
OCR A	C5	✓
OCR B	C4, C5	✓
EDEXCEL	C1, C2	✓
CCEA	C1, C2	✓

Some insoluble salts can be made from the reaction between two solutions. Barium sulfate is an insoluble salt. It can be made by the reaction between solutions of barium chloride and sodium sulfate.

barium chloride + sodium sulfate → barium sulfate + sodium chloride

BaCl$_2$(aq) + Na$_2$SO$_4$(aq) → BaSO$_4$(s) + 2NaCl(aq)

Understanding precipitation reactions

AQA	C1, C2 ✓
OCR A	C5 ✓
OCR B	C4, C5 ✓
EDEXCEL	C1, C2 ✓
CCEA	C1, C2 ✓

The insoluble barium sulfate can be filtered off, washed and dried. Overall, the two original salts, barium chloride and sodium sulfate, have swapped partners. Barium chloride solution can be used to test whether a solution contains sulfate ions. If sulfate ions are present, a white precipitate of barium sulfate will be seen. The chloride ions and sodium ions are **spectator ions**. They are present but they are not involved in the reaction. The ionic equation for the reaction is:

$$Ba^{2+}(aq) + SO_4^{2-}(aq) \rightarrow BaSO_4(s)$$

Precipitation reactions are very fast. When the reactant solutions are mixed, the reacting ions collide together very quickly and react together to form the insoluble solid.

Barium sulfate is used in medicine as a **barium meal**. The patient is given the insoluble salt and then X-rayed. The barium sulfate is opaque to X-rays so doctors can detect digestive problems without having to carry out an operation. Although barium salts are toxic, barium sulfate is so insoluble that very little dissolves and passes into the bloodstream of the patient.

PROGRESS CHECK

1. Why must there be the same number of each type of atom on both sides of an equation?
2. Balance the equation $Na + Cl_2 \rightarrow NaCl$.
3. Balance the equation $H_2 + Cl_2 \rightarrow HCl$.
4. Balance the equation $C + CO_2 \rightarrow CO$.
5. What does the state symbol (l) indicate?
6. Explain why precipitation reactions happen very quickly.

1. Atoms cannot be created or destroyed during chemical reactions.
2. $2Na + Cl_2 \rightarrow 2NaCl$.
3. $H_2 + Cl_2 \rightarrow 2HCl$.
4. $C + CO_2 \rightarrow 2CO$.
5. It is a liquid.
6. The reacting ions collide together and react very quickly

1.6 Ionic and covalent bonding

LEARNING SUMMARY

After studying this section, you should be able to:

- Describe the differences between ionic and covalent bonding.
- Predict the type of ion formed, by looking at electron arrangements.
- Draw diagrams to show the ionic bonding in simple ionic compounds.
- Explain how non-metal atoms bond by sharing pairs of electrons.
- Draw diagrams to show electron sharing in simple covalent molecules.

Types of bonding

AQA	C1, C2	✓
OCR A	C5	✓
OCR B	C1–C6	✓
EDEXCEL	C2	✓
WJEC	C1, C2	✓
CCEA	C1	✓

Compounds are made when **atoms** of two or more **elements** are chemically combined. **Ionic bonding** involves the transfer of **electrons** in the outermost shell of atoms. This forms **ions** with opposite charges, which then attract each other. Ions are atoms or groups of atoms with a charge. **Covalent bonding** involves the sharing of electrons. The attraction of the nuclei for shared pairs of electrons hold the atoms together.

Ionic bonding

AQA	C1, C2	✓
OCR A	C5	✓
OCR B	C1–C6	✓
EDEXCEL	C2	✓
WJEC	C1, C2	✓
CCEA	C1	✓

KEY POINT

Atoms react to get a full outer shell of electrons (like the noble gas elements). Ionic bonding involves the transfer of electrons from one atom to another.

Metal atoms in groups 1 and 2, such as sodium or calcium, lose electrons to get a full outer shell of electrons. Overall, they become positively charged. (Electrons have a negative charge). Non-metal atoms in groups 6 and 7, such as oxygen or chlorine, gain electrons to get a full outer shell. They become negatively charged. An ion is an atom, or a group of atoms, with a charge. An atom, or group of atoms, becomes an ion by gaining or losing electrons. The positive and negative ions formed have the same electronic structure as a noble gas atom.

Ionic compounds

AQA	C2	✓
OCR A	C4, C5	✓
OCR B	C1–C6	✓
EDEXCEL	C2, C3	✓
WJEC	C1, C2	✓
CCEA	C1	✓

Compound	Diagram	Comments
sodium + chlorine → sodium chloride	In the dot and cross diagrams, the electrons drawn as dots, and the electrons drawn as crosses, are identical. They are drawn like this so it is easier to see what happens when the electrons move.	The sodium atom transfers one electron from its outer shell to the chlorine atom. Both the sodium and chlorine atom have a full outer shell. The sodium atom has lost a negatively charged electron so it now has a 1+ charge and is called a sodium ion. The chlorine atom has gained an electron so has a 1- charge. It is now a chloride ion. The attraction between these two oppositely charged ions is called an ionic bond and it holds the compound together.

1 Atoms and materials

Compound	Diagram	Comments
magnesium + oxygen → magnesium oxide		The magnesium atom transfers two electrons from its outer shell to the oxygen atom. Both the magnesium and oxygen atoms have a full outer shell. The magnesium atom has lost two electrons so has a 2+ charge. It is now a magnesium ion. The oxygen atom has gained two electrons so has a 2- charge. It is now an oxide ion. The attraction between these two oppositely charged ions is called an ionic bond and it holds the compound together.
calcium + chlorine → calcium chloride This is an alternative way of drawing a dot and cross diagram. You only draw the outer shell.		The calcium atom transfers two electrons from its outer shell to two chlorine atoms. Both the calcium and chlorine atoms have a full outer shell. The calcium atom has lost two electrons so has a 2+ charge. It is now a calcium ion. The chlorine atoms have gained one electron each so have a 1- charge. They are now chloride ions. The attraction between these two oppositely charged ions is called an ionic bond and it holds the compound together.

Sodium oxide has the formula Na_2O. Both sodium atoms transfer one electron to the same oxygen atom. The sodium ions each have a 1+ charge while the oxide ion has a 2- charge.

Covalent bonding

AQA	C2	✓
OCR A	C5	✓
OCR B	C1–C6	✓
EDEXCEL	C2	✓
WJEC	C2	✓
CCEA	C1	✓

KEY POINT

Covalent bonding occurs between atoms of non-metal elements. The atoms share pairs of electrons so that all the atoms gain a full outer shell of electrons.

There is an **electrostatic attraction** between the nuclei of the atoms and the pair of bonding electrons.

Covalent molecules

AQA	C1, C2	✓
OCR A	C4	✓
OCR B	C1–C6	✓
EDEXCEL	C2	✓
WJEC	C2	✓
CCEA	C1	✓

Compound	Diagram of molecule	Comments
Hydrogen		Both the hydrogen atoms have just one electron. Both atoms can get a full outer shell by sharing these electrons to form a single covalent bond.
Hydrogen chloride		The hydrogen atom and the chlorine atom both need one more electron. They share a pair of electrons to form a single covalent bond, so they now both have a full outer shell.
Methane		The carbon atom has four electrons in its outer shell so it needs four more electrons to have a full shell. The carbon shares one pair of electrons with four different hydrogen atoms to form four single covalent bonds. Now all the atoms have a full outer shell.
Ammonia		The nitrogen atom has five outer electrons so it needs three more electrons for a full shell. It gains these electrons by sharing a pair of electrons with three hydrogen atoms to form three single covalent bonds.
Oxygen		Both oxygen atoms have six outer electrons so they need a share of two more electrons. They gain these by sharing two pairs of electrons to form a double covalent bond.

PROGRESS CHECK

1. What are ions?
2. What holds the atoms together in covalent molecules?
3. What happens to electrons during ionic bonding?
4. What type of atom is oxygen?
5. Name and describe the type of bonding that you would expect to find in these substances:
   a) Oxygen O_2.
   b) Sodium chloride, NaCl.

PROGRESS CHECK

chloride ions.
b) Ionic bonding between the positively charged sodium ions and the negatively charged
5. a) Covalent bonding, with a double bond covalent between the two oxygen atoms.
4. Non-metal.
3. Electrons are transferred.
2. Shared pairs of electrons.
1. Atoms or groups of atoms with a charge.

1.7 Ionic and covalent structures

LEARNING SUMMARY

After studying this section, you should be able to:

- Describe ionic bonding and compounds.
- Describe simple covalent structures and their properties.
- Describe giant covalent structures and their properties.
- Describe the structure and properties of diamond.
- Describe the structure and properties of graphite.

Ionic bonding

AQA	C2	✓
OCR A	C4	✓
OCR B	C1–C6	✓
EDEXCEL	C2	✓
WJEC	C1, C2	✓
CCEA	C1	✓

KEY POINT

Ionic bonding occurs between metal and non-metal atoms. It involves the transfer of **electrons** and the formation of **ions**.

Sodium chloride and magnesium oxide are examples of ionic compounds. The ions are arranged in a regular 'lattice' with each positive ion surrounded by negative ions and vice versa.

Ionic compounds

AQA	C2	✓
OCR A	C4, C5	✓
OCR B	C1–C6	✓
EDEXCEL	C2	✓
WJEC	C1, C2	✓
CCEA	C1	✓

- **Ionic compounds** are held together by the strong forces of attraction between oppositely charged ions (electrostatic attraction).
- Ionic compounds have a regular structure.
- The **strong** forces of attraction between oppositely charged ions work in all directions and this means that ionic compounds have high melting and boiling points.
- When dissolved in water, ionic compounds form solutions in which the ions can move. This means that these solutions can **conduct** electricity.
- Similarly, if ionic compounds are heated up so that they melt, the ions can move. Molten ionic compounds can also conduct electricity.

Simple covalent structures

AQA	C2	✓
OCR A	C5	✓
OCR B	C1, C4	✓
EDEXCEL	C2	✓
WJEC	C2	✓
CCEA	C1	✓

Covalent bonding occurs between non-metal atoms. It involves the sharing of electrons. Examples of simple covalent structures include:

- chlorine molecules
- oxygen molecules
- hydrogen iodide molecules
- methane molecules
- water molecules
- carbon dioxide molecules.

These **molecules** are all formed from small numbers of atoms.

Important properties of simple molecular compounds

AQA	C2	✓
OCR A	C5	✓
OCR B	C4	✓
EDEXCEL	C2	✓
WJEC	C2	✓
CCEA	C1	✓

> **KEY POINT**
>
> There are very strong covalent bonds between the atoms in each molecule, but very weak forces of attraction between these molecules.

The low boiling points of simple molecules is due to the weak forces of attraction between molecules.

This means that simple molecular compounds have low melting and boiling points. Most are gases or liquids at room temperature. Simple molecular compounds do not conduct electricity because, unlike ions, the molecules do not have an overall electrical charge. They tend to be **insoluble** in water (although they may dissolve in water and other solvents).

To help you learn the facts you need for the exam, make a table to compare the features of ionic and covalent structures.

Giant covalent structures

AQA	C2	✓
OCR A	C5	✓
OCR B	C3	✓
EDEXCEL	C2	✓
WJEC	C2	✓
CCEA	C1	✓

Examples of giant covalent (macromolecular) structures include:

- diamond
- graphite
- silicon dioxide.

These structures are formed from a large number of atoms. All the atoms in these structures are held together by **strong covalent bonds**. This means that these substances have **high melting and boiling points**. They are solids at room temperature. Like simple covalent molecules, giant covalent substances do not conduct electricity (except graphite) as they do not contain ions. They are also **insoluble** in water.

Diamond

AQA	C2	✓
OCR A	C5	✓
OCR B	C3	✓
EDEXCEL	C2	✓
WJEC	C2	✓
CCEA	C1	✓

Diamond is a form of the element carbon. Like other gemstones, it is prized for its rarity and its pleasing appearance: it is lustrous, colourless and transparent. Diamond is also very hard. High quality diamonds are used to make jewellery. Other diamonds are used in industry in a variety of applications. The hardness and high melting point of diamond makes it very suitable for cutting tools. The special properties of diamond are the result of its **structure**. Diamond is an example of a giant covalent substance. Each carbon atom is bonded to four other carbon atoms by strong covalent bonds. It takes a lot of energy to break these strong bonds. Diamond is a very poor electrical conductor because it does not have any free electrons.

Diamond structure

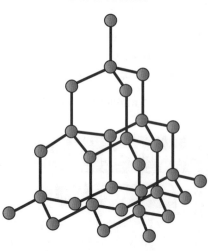

Graphite

AQA	C2	✓
OCR A	C5	✓
OCR B	C3	✓
EDEXCEL	C2	✓
WJEC	C2	✓
CCEA	C1	✓

Graphite is another **allotrope** of the element carbon. Allotropes are different forms of the same element in the same physical state. Diamond, graphite and fullerene are all allotropes of carbon. Graphite is black, lustrous and opaque. It is used to make pencil 'leads' because the layers slip apart easily, so when a pencil is rubbed on paper a black mark is left. It is also used in lubricants because it is slippery and allows surfaces to pass over each other more easily.

In graphite, each carbon atom forms strong covalent bonds with three other carbon atoms in the same layer. However, the bonding between layers is much weaker. This means that the layers can pass over each other quite easily, which is why graphite is soft and feels greasy. If a potential difference is applied across graphite the electrons in the weak bonds between layers move and so conduct electricity. Carbon in the form of graphite is the only non-metal element that conducts electricity. It also has a very high melting point because a lot of energy is required to break these strong covalent bonds. These properties make it a suitable material from which to make electrodes.

PROGRESS CHECK

1. What type of structure is magnesium oxide?
2. What type of structure is graphite?
3. What type of structure is methane?
4. What type of structure is diamond?
5. Sodium chloride is an ionic compound. It does not conduct electricity when solid but does when it is dissolved in water. Explain these observations in terms of the particles involved.

PROGRESS CHECK

5. Sodium chloride contains sodium ions and chloride ions. The ions cannot move when it is solid, so solid sodium chloride does not conduct electricity. When the sodium chloride is dissolved in water the ions can move, so aqueous sodium chloride does conduct electricity.
4. Giant covalent.
3. Simple covalent/molecular.
2. Giant covalent.
1. Ionic compound.

1.8 Group 7

LEARNING SUMMARY

After studying this section, you should be able to:

- Recall that elements in group 7 have seven outer-shell electrons.
- Describe trends in physical properties of group 7 elements.
- Recall the uses of some halogen elements.
- Describe and explain the trend in reactivity of the halogens.
- Use differences in reactivity to explain halogen displacement reactions.

The halogens

AQA	C2, C3	✓
OCR A	C4	✓
OCR B	C4	✓
EDEXCEL	C2	✓
WJEC	C1, C2	✓
CCEA	C1	✓

The elements in group 7 are known as the **halogens**. The atoms of group 7 elements all have seven electrons in their outermost shell. When halogen atoms react they gain an electron to form **halide ions**.

Characteristics of the halogens

AQA	C3	✓
OCR A	C4	✓
OCR B	C4	✓
EDEXCEL	C2	✓
WJEC	C1, C2	✓
CCEA	C1	✓

Down the group, the melting points and boiling points of the halogens increase, so fluorine and chlorine are gases at room temperature while bromine is a liquid and iodine is a solid. Halogens react with hydrogen to form hydrogen halides, for example, chlorine reacts with hydrogen to form hydrogen chloride. Hydrogen halides dissolve in water to form acidic solutions.

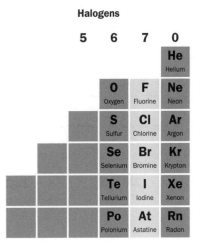

Halogens

The halogen family includes fluorine, chlorine, bromine and iodine. Halogens have coloured vapours. The colour gets darker further down the group.

Halogen	Comments
Fluorine	Fluorine is a very poisonous gas that should only be used in a **fume cupboard**. Fluorine is a **diatomic** (two atoms joined together) molecule with the formula F_2. It has a pale yellow colour. Sodium fluoride is added to toothpastes and to some water supplies to help prevent tooth decay. Scientists carried out large studies to prove that adding fluoride compounds was effective at protecting teeth, but some people are concerned over the lack of choice those living in affected areas now have.
Chlorine	Chlorine is a poisonous gas that should only be used in a fume cupboard. Chlorine is a diatomic molecule with the formula Cl_2. It has a pale green colour. Chlorine kills bacteria and is used in water purification. It is also used to make plastics and pesticides and in **bleaching**. In the past, chlorine and iodine were extracted from compounds found in seawater. However, it is no longer economically worthwhile to extract iodine in this way.
Bromine	Bromine is a poisonous, dense liquid. It has a brown colour. Bromine is a diatomic molecule, Br_2.
Iodine	Iodine exists as a dark grey crystalline solid. Solid iodine is brittle and crumbly. Solid iodine is a poor electrical and thermal conductor. Iodine forms a purple vapour when warmed. Iodine solution can be used as an antiseptic to sterilise wounds as it kills bacteria. Iodine solution can be used to test for the presence of starch. When iodine solution is placed on a material that contains starch it turns blue/black. Iodine is a diatomic molecule, I_2.
Astatine	Astatine is also in group 7 of the periodic table; it is found just below iodine. We can use the physical properties of the other halogens to predict the properties of astatine. It will be a dark coloured solid at room temperature.

Be careful not to write chloride if you mean chlorine.

To help you learn the facts about halogens, try making a poster with a different section for each member of the group.

Why halogens react in a similar way

AQA	C2, C3	✓
OCR A	C4	✓
OCR B	C4	✓
EDEXCEL	C2	✓
WJEC	C1, C2	✓
CCEA	C1	✓

KEY POINT

Halogens have seven electrons in their outer shell. Group 7 elements have similar properties because they all have similar electron structures. Halogens react with metal atoms to form ionic compounds.

For example, chlorine reacts with potassium to form potassium chloride.

chlorine + potassium → potassium chloride

$$2K + Cl_2 \rightarrow 2KCl$$

Reduction

AQA	C3	✓
OCR A	C4	✓
OCR B	C4	✓
EDEXCEL	C2	✓
WJEC	C2	✓
CCEA	C1	✓

When they react, a halogen atom gains an electron to form an ion with a 1– charge.

$$Cl + e^- \rightarrow Cl^-$$

A reduction reaction has taken place. The halogen atom has gained an electron so it is **reduced**.

Important trends

AQA	C3	✓
OCR A	C4	✓
OCR B	C4	✓
EDEXCEL	C2	✓
WJEC	C1, C2	✓
CCEA	C1	✓

Melting and boiling points increase down the group. Group 7 atoms form molecules in which two atoms are joined together. These are called diatomic molecules.

Down the group, the atoms get larger and have more electrons. This means that the strength of the attraction between molecules increases. As the forces of attraction between molecules get stronger down the group, it takes more energy to overcome these forces so the halogens will melt and boil at higher temperatures.

Why fluorine reacts more vigorously than bromine

AQA	C3	✓
OCR A	C4	✓
OCR B	C4	✓
EDEXCEL	C2	✓
WJEC	C2	✓
CCEA	C2	✓

Reactivity decreases down the group: when an atom reacts to form an **ion**, the new electron is being placed into a shell further away from the nucleus. So, down the group, it is harder for atoms to gain an electron. There are also more shells of electrons shielding the new electron from the nucleus. This also makes it harder for atoms to gain a new electron further down the group. This pattern is clearly shown by the reaction between the halogens and iron wool to form iron halides.

Chlorine is more reactive than bromine and iodine.

Halogen used	Observations
Chlorine	Iron glows very brightly. A brown smoke is given off and a brown solid is formed.
Bromine	The iron glows. Brown smoke is given off and a brown solid is formed.
Iodine	The iron glows a little. Brown smoke is given off and a brown solid is formed.

Reactivity of halogens

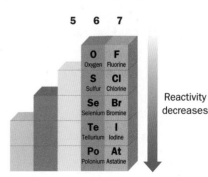

Reactivity decreases

Displacement reactions involving halogens

AQA	C3	✓
OCR A	C4	✓
OCR B	C4	✓
EDEXCEL	C2	✓
WJEC	C2	✓
CCEA	C1	✓

KEY POINT

Reactivity decreases down group 7. The most reactive halogen is fluorine, followed by chlorine, then bromine, then iodine.

A more reactive halogen will **displace** (that is, take the place of) a less reactive halogen from an aqueous solution of its salt. So, chlorine could displace bromine or iodine. However, while bromine could displace iodine it could not displace chlorine.

Symbol equations

OCR A	C4	✓
OCR B	C1–C6	✓
EDEXCEL	C2	✓
WJEC	C2	✓
CCEA	C2	✓

Chlorine will displace iodine from a solution of potassium iodide.

chlorine + potassium iodide → iodine + potassium chloride

$$Cl_2 + 2KI \rightarrow I_2 + 2KCl$$

The reaction between chlorine and potassium iodide

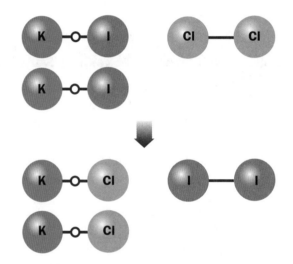

PROGRESS CHECK

1. What is the name given to group 7 of the periodic table?
2. How is a halide ion formed?
3. What type of compound is formed when a metal reacts with a halogen?
4. What is the name of the compound made when chlorine reacts with potassium?
5. Chlorine gas is passed through an aqueous solution of potassium iodide. Write a word and symbol equation to sum up this reaction. Remember to include state symbols in your answer.

1. Halogens.
2. When a halogen atom gains an electron
3. Ionic compound/metal halide.
4. Potassium chloride.
5. chlorine + potassium iodide → iodine + potassium chloride
$Cl_2(g) + 2KI(aq) \rightarrow I_2(aq) + 2KCl(aq)$

1.9 New materials

LEARNING SUMMARY

After studying this section, you should be able to:

- Understand that new materials need to be developed for new uses.
- Describe the properties of photochromic and thermochromic materials.
- Relate the properties of new materials to their uses.
- Understand the properties of nanomaterials.
- Relate the properties of nanomaterials to their uses.

Smart materials

AQA	C1	✓
WJEC	C2	✓

Many scientists are involved in making new materials. These materials can have very special properties. Smart materials have one or more property that can be dramatically and reversibly altered by changes in the environment. A whole variety of smart materials already exist including:

- shape-memory alloys
- thermochromic materials
- photochromic materials.

Scientists are working to find more applications for existing smart materials and to discover new materials.

Photochromic materials

Photochromic materials change colour when exposed to bright light. They are widely used to make lenses for glasses. The lenses adapt to light conditions: when it is bright, the lenses get darker.

Photochromic glasses

Hydrogels

Hydrogels are a new type of polymer. They are able to absorb water and swell up as the result of changes in pH or changes in temperature. Hydrogels are being used to make special wound dressings. Hydrogels help to:

- stop fluid loss from the wound
- absorb bacteria and odour molecules
- cool and cushion the wound
- reduce the number of times the wound has to be disturbed (e.g. to change the dressing).

The hydrogel is transparent, so medical staff can monitor the wound without having to remove the dressing.

Nanoparticles

AQA	C2	✓
OCR A	C2	✓
WJEC	C1	✓
CCEA	C2	✓

> **KEY POINT**
>
> Nanoscience is the study of extremely small pieces of material called nanoparticles.

Scientists are currently researching the properties of new nanoparticles. These are substances that contain just a few hundred atoms and vary in size from 1 nm (nanometre) to 100 nm so they are the same size as some molecules (human hair has a width of about 100 000 nm). Nanoparticles occur in nature and are found in sea spray. They can also be made either accidentally, for example, when fuels are burned, or very deliberately.

Nanomaterials have unique properties because of the very precise way in which the atoms are arranged. Scientists have found that many materials behave differently on such a small scale.

> In nanomaterials, the atoms themselves are not smaller. When you answer exam questions, make sure you do not infer that the atoms have changed size.

Scientists are using nanoparticles to develop very lightweight materials. These materials are incredibly hard and strong because of the precise way that the atoms are arranged. One day these materials could be used to build planes.

Nanoparticles have a very high surface area to volume ratio. Scientists hope that this will allow them to use nanoparticles in exciting ways such as:

- in new computers
- in sunscreens and deodorants
- in drug delivery systems
- better catalysts. Catalysts are substances that speed up the rate of a chemical reaction but are not themselves used up. Reactions take place at the surface of the catalyst. The larger the surface area of the catalyst the more reactions can take place at once and the better the catalyst performs.

Scientists are also keen to explore the use of nanoparticles as sensors to detect biological or chemical agents at very low levels. They may also be used to make battery electrodes for electric vehicles or solar cells.

Nanoscale silver particles have antibacterial, antiviral and antifungal properties. These tiny pieces of silver are incorporated into materials to make clothes and medical dressings stay fresh for longer.

> Try producing a set of revision cards to learn the important ideas in this topic.

There has recently been a great deal of media interest in the development and applications of new nanoparticles. Some scientists are concerned that certain nanoparticles could be dangerous to people because their exceptionally small size may mean they are able to pass into the body in previously unimaginable ways, and could go on to cause health problems.

Buckminster fullerene, C_{60}

| AQA | C2 | ✓ |
| OCR B | C3 | ✓ |

The element carbon exists in three forms or allotropes:

- graphite
- diamond
- fullerenes.

Fullerenes are structures made when carbon atoms join together to form tubes, balls or cages, which are held together by strong covalent bonds. The most symmetrical and, therefore, most stable example is buckminster fullerene. This consists of 60 carbon atoms joined together in a series of hexagons and pentagons, much like a leather football.

Structure of buckminster fullerene

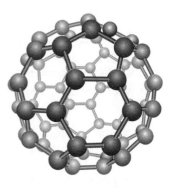

Learn the formula for buckminster fullerene:
C_{60}

PROGRESS CHECK

1. Why are smart materials special?
2. How big are nanoparticles?
3. What is the formula of buckminster fullerene?
4. Where are nanoparticles found in nature?
5. What is special about a photochromic material?

5. Photochromic materials change colour when exposed to bright light.
4. In sea spray.
3. C_{60}.
2. 1 nm–100 nm.
1. They have one or more property that responds to changes in the environment.

1.10 Synthesis

LEARNING SUMMARY

After studying this section, you should be able to:

- Understand that making new chemicals involves many stages.
- Describe the differences between batch and continuous manufacturing processes.
- Recall that plants are often good sources of chemicals.
- Understand the economics and licensing involved in developing a new medicine.
- List the factors affecting the long-term sustainability of a chemical process.

Making new chemicals

OCR A	C2, C6,	✓
	C7	✓
OCR B	C2, C3,	✓
	C6	✓

The manufacture of useful chemicals involves many stages. **Raw materials** need to be selected and prepared, and then the new chemicals have to be made in a process known as **synthesis**. Next, the useful products have to be separated from **by-products** and waste, each of which must also be dealt with. Finally, the **purity** of the product must be checked.

Batch or continuous production

OCR A   C7   ✓
OCR B   C3, C6   ✓

Some chemicals are made in **batch processes**.

> **KEY POINT**
>
> Batch processes are used to make relatively small amounts of special chemicals such as medicines. The chemicals are made when they are needed rather than all the time.
>
> **Continuous processes** are used to make chemicals that are needed in large amounts, such as sulfuric acid or ammonia.

The chemicals are made all the time. Raw materials are continuously added and new products are removed.

Some chemicals, such as ammonia, sulfuric acid, sodium hydroxide and phosphoric acid, are made in **bulk** (on a large scale). Other chemicals, such as medicines, food additives and fragrances, are described as being made on a **fine** scale (a small scale).

Governments regulate how chemicals are made, stored and transported to protect people and the environment from accidental damage.

Medicines from plants

OCR B   C3   ✓

Scientists can **extract** chemicals from plants or produce them synthetically. Chemicals can be extracted from plants by:

> Make a flow diagram to show the stages involved in extracting chemicals from plants.

- Crushing up the plant material.
- Adding a suitable solvent and then heating the mixture so that the useful chemicals dissolve in the solvent.
- Using separation techniques, such as chromatography, to separate out mixtures of compounds. Chromatography separates mixtures according to differences in solubility of the components.

Plant materials can be used to make very useful medicines. Digitalin medicines are extracted from foxglove plants and are used to treat heart conditions.

Digitalin can be extracted from foxglove plants

Morphine is made from opium poppies and is used for pain relief.

Opium poppy pod and seeds, from which morphine can be made

Making and developing new medicines

OCR B   C3   ✓

New medicines are often very expensive to buy because of the high costs of **developing** and making the drugs. The factors that affect the price of a medicine include:

- Labour and energy costs. The production of new medicines is often very labour intensive as little automation is possible, at least initially.
- The cost of the raw materials required, which may be very rare or expensive.
- The time required for researching and developing new drugs. These processes can take many years.
- Testing of the new medicine. It must pass all the testing stages and human trials required by law for it to gain a licence to be sold. This takes a lot of time and money.
- Marketing of the medicine. Companies have to let the medical profession know the benefits of the new medicine and why they should consider giving it to their patients.

Economic considerations

OCR B   C3   ✓

Scientists developing new drugs need to be aware of economic considerations. The more research and development involved the more expensive the new medicine will be. Scientists need to work out if there is sufficient demand for the new medicine for it to pay back the considerable investment needed to produce it. New drugs only have a patent for a certain length of time. Companies that manufacture the medicine pay money to the people who hold the patent and who did the initial research and development for the drug. If the time limit for the patent is set too low, the patent will have run out before the initial costs have been paid back.

Green chemistry

| OCR A | C7 | ✓ |
| OCR B | C3 | ✓ |

Addition reactions (when two chemicals are added together), such as the reaction between ethene and steam to produce ethanol, will have an atom economy of 100%

The long-term sustainability of a chemical process depends on:

- whether or not the raw materials are renewable
- the atom economy of the reactions involved
- the amount and nature of waste produced
- the amount and nature of by-products produced
- energy requirements
- impact on the environment
- health and safety risks
- the economic and social benefits of the products made by the reaction.

PROGRESS CHECK

1. Why are the labour costs for new medicines often very high?
2. Why do new drugs have to be marketed?
3. Name a separation technique that separates out mixtures because the components have different solubilities.
4. Name two types of medicine that are made using plant extracts.
5. Describe the steps involved in extracting chemicals from plants.
6. Describe what happens during a continuous process.

1. Little automation is possible, at least initially.
2. To let the medical profession know the benefits of the new medicine and why they should consider giving it to their patients.
3. Chromatography.
4. Digitalin medicines and morphine.
5. Crush up the plant material. Add a suitable solvent and then heat the mixture so that the useful chemicals dissolve in the solvent. Use separation techniques, such as chromatography, to separate out mixtures of compounds.
6. The chemicals are made all the time. Raw materials are continuously added and new products are removed.

Sample GCSE questions

1 Use the periodic table in the data sheet to help answer these questions.

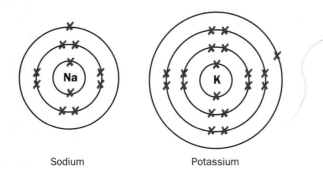

Sodium   Potassium

a) (i) Complete the diagrams to show the electron arrangements of both atoms. **[2]**

Mark the electrons as clear Xs on the circles. Sodium should have the arrangement 2, 8, 1, while potassium has the arrangement 2, 8, 8, 1. Remember shells fill from the inside outwards.

(ii) Why are sodium and potassium in the same group of the periodic table? **[1]**

Both atoms have the same number of electrons in their outer shells, i.e. one electron.

Remember that the number of outer shell electrons is the same as the group number.

(iii) Why are sodium and potassium in different periods on the periodic table? **[1]**

Sodium has three shells containing electrons, while potassium has four.

Remember that the period number is the same as the number of shells the atom has.

(b) Sodium has mass number 23, potassium has mass number 39.

(i) How many protons are in an atom of sodium? **[1]**

11

Be careful! The number of protons is the same as the number of electrons you drew in part a(i). The mass number is not needed to calculate the number of protons!

(ii) How many neutrons are in an atom of potassium? **[1]**

The number of neutrons is mass number – atomic number: 39 - 19 = 20 neutrons.

(c) Sodium metal reacts with water to produce hydrogen gas and sodium hydroxide:

$$2Na(s) + 2H_2O(l) \rightarrow 2NaOH(aq) + H_2(g)$$

If you read the question properly, you will notice that it is now asking about potassium, not sodium.

(i) Which gas would be produced when potassium reacts with water? **[1]**

Hydrogen.

Elements in the same group have similar reactions, so the gas will be hydrogen again.

Sample GCSE questions

(ii) Give the name and formula of the other product. **[1]**

> *If sodium produces sodium hydroxide, potassium will produce potassium hydroxide.*

> *The formula for potassium hydroxide is KOH.*

Check the symbol for potassium, using the periodic table, before writing the formula (it is K!)

The formula doesn't need a 2 in front, because you aren't balancing an equation.

2 (a) A company called 'Moreco' wants to manufacture and market a new painkiller based on a compound originally extracted from a rare South American plant. Scientists at Moreco have managed to synthesise a similar compound, which has the same painkilling properties.

(i) Why has Moreco produced a synthetic version of the compound, rather than using the original plant extract?
[2]

> *Moreco have developed a synthetic alternative so that they are not dependent on such a limited raw material and to keep costs down.*

Always read the information given: it tells you the plant is 'rare' and that it grows in South America.

(ii) Why should the Moreco painkiller be thoroughly tested before a licence is given for the company to market their product?
[2]

> *The product must be safe for humans to take. It must be free from unwanted side-effects.*

When phrasing your answer, you should mention that safety is in relation to human consumption, and that side-effects may otherwise cause problems.

(iii) Why is it better that the testing of the painkiller is carried out independently, rather than by Moreco's own scientists?
[2]

> *The scientists working for Moreco may be biased, because Moreco will profit from the licence being given. Independent scientists would not be biased.*

When answering any question where you have to compare two alternatives, always try to comment on both in your answer.

(b) Apart from the cost of testing the product, to ensure it is safe for human consumption, what other costs would Moreco have to take into account when deciding the selling price for their new painkiller?
[4]

> *Any four from:*
> * *cost of raw materials to make the product*
> * *research and development costs in the initial stages*
> * *energy costs involved in production*
> * *advertising and marketing costs*
> * *packaging and distribution costs*

Where you have a lot of space for a number of marks, it is best to bullet-point your answers.

Exam practice questions

1 The nucleus of a neon atom has 10 protons and 10 neutrons.

(a) What is the atomic number of neon? .... **[1]**

(b) What is the atomic mass of a neon atom? .... **[1]**

(c) What is the electron arrangement of a neon atom? .... **[1]**

(d) Where would you expect to find neon on the periodic table? **[2]**

....

....

2 The compound, calcium carbonate, has the formula $CaCO_3$.

(a) How many chemical elements have combined in calcium carbonate?

.... **[1]**

(b) How many atoms, in total, are represented by the formula $CaCO_3$?

.... **[1]**

(c) A calcium ion has the formula Ca^{2+}: how is it different from a calcium atom?

.... **[2]**

(d) What is the charge on a carbonate ion: $CO_3^?$?

.... **[1]**

3 An outline of the modern Periodic Table is shown:

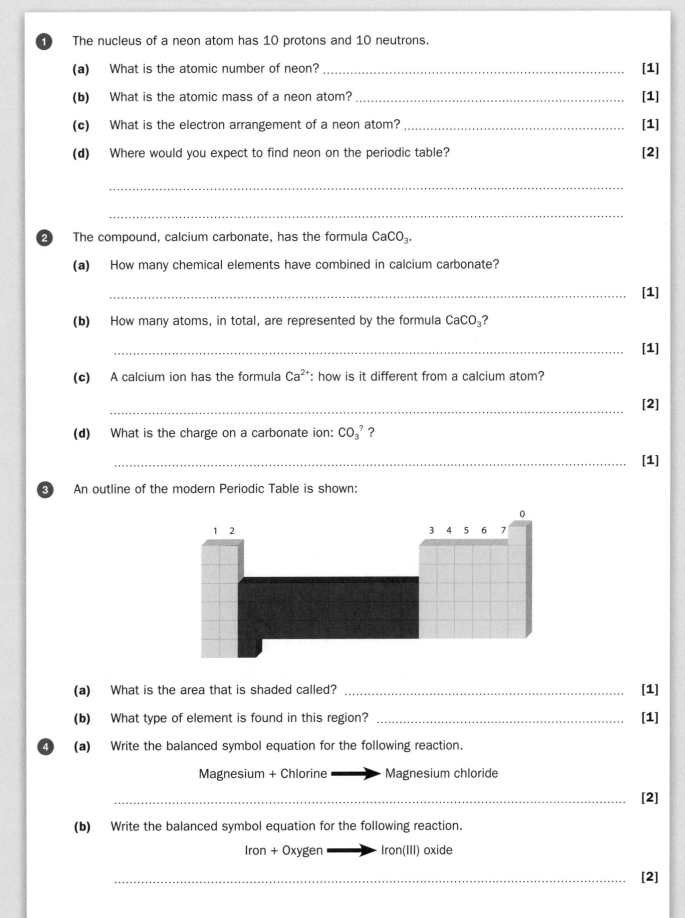

(a) What is the area that is shaded called? .... **[1]**

(b) What type of element is found in this region? .... **[1]**

4 **(a)** Write the balanced symbol equation for the following reaction.

Magnesium + Chlorine ⟶ Magnesium chloride

.... **[2]**

(b) Write the balanced symbol equation for the following reaction.

Iron + Oxygen ⟶ Iron(III) oxide

.... **[2]**

Exam practice questions

5 In the production of ammonia, nitrogen reacts with hydrogen according to this equation:

$N_2(g)$ + ... $H_2(g)$ → .... $NH_3(g)$

(a) In which physical state are the reactants and products?

.... [1]

(b) What do we call a particle of nitrogen where two atoms are bonded together?

.... [1]

(c) Balance the equation by putting numbers into the gaps.

.... [2]

(d) Suggest what ammonia would react with to make ammonium hydroxide, NH_4OH.

.... [1]

6 Chlorine is an element that bonds ionically with metal elements or covalently with non-metal elements. A chlorine atom has seven electrons in its outer shell.

(a) How many electrons does chlorine need in a full outer shell?

.... [1]

(b) Deduce the formula of a chloride ion.

.... [1]

(c) How many electrons are shared in a molecule of chlorine?

.... [1]

(d) Draw a diagram of a molecule of chlorine, showing outer shell electrons only. [2]

7 Diamond and graphite are two different forms of carbon. Describe the structure and properties of:

(a) diamond

....

....

.... [3]

(b) graphite.

....

....

.... [3]

Exam practice questions

8 The elements of group 7 are called the halogens.

(a) What happens to the melting points of halogens as you go down the group?

.... **[1]**

(b) What happens to the reactivity of halogens as you go down the group?

.... **[1]**

(c) Explain the trend in reactivity in terms of the structure of halogen atoms.

....

.... **[2]**

9 **(a)** Pharmaceutical drugs are made using a batch process.

Explain why the materials needed to make new medicines are expensive.

....

.... **[1]**

(b) Describe the advantages of using a batch process to make a chemical.

....

....

.... **[3]**

10 Magnesium oxide is an ionically bonded compound. It contains magnesium ions: Mg^{2+}, and oxide ions: O^{2-}.

Describe the properties you would expect magnesium oxide to have, making it clear how you are able to make these deductions from the information that is given.

The quality of written communication will be assessed in your answer to this question.

....

....

....

....

....

....

....

....

.... **[6]**

2 The Earth and pollution

The following topics are covered in this chapter:

- Evolution of the atmosphere
- Noble gases and the fractional distillation of air
- Pollution of the atmosphere
- The greenhouse effect and ozone depletion
- Pollution of the environment
- Evidence of plate tectonics
- Consequences of plate tectonics
- Everyday chemistry
- The carbon cycle

2.1 Evolution of the atmosphere

LEARNING SUMMARY

After studying this section, you should be able to:

- Describe the composition of the Earth's early atmosphere.
- Compare the early atmosphere to today's atmosphere.
- Relate changes in the atmosphere to specific processes.
- Understand the significance of the Miller-Urey experiment.
- List natural processes that reduce atmospheric carbon dioxide.

The atmosphere today

AQA	C1	✓
OCR A	C1, C5	✓
OCR B	C1	✓
EDEXCEL	C1	✓
WJEC	C1	✓
CCEA	C2	✓

> **KEY POINT**
>
> Today, the **atmosphere** is composed of: about 78% **nitrogen**, about 21% **oxygen**, small amounts of **other gases**, such as carbon dioxide, water vapour and **noble gases**, for example, argon and neon.

Carbon dioxide, CO_2 (0.03%)

Mainly argon, plus other noble gases (1%)

Oxygen, O_2 (21%)

Nitrogen, N_2 (78%)

Changes in the atmosphere

AQA	C1	✓
OCR A	C1	✓
OCR B	C1	✓
EDEXCEL	C1	✓
WJEC	C1	✓
CCEA	C2	✓

Small changes in today's atmosphere can be caused by **volcanic activity** or by human activities, such as **deforestation** or farming. Throughout the history of the Earth, the composition of the atmosphere has changed.

The first billion years

During the first billion years of the Earth's life, there was enormous volcanic activity. Volcanoes belched out carbon dioxide (CO_2), steam or water vapour (H_2O), ammonia (NH_3) and methane (CH_4). The atmosphere consisted mainly of carbon dioxide and there was very little oxygen. In fact, Earth's atmosphere was very similar to the atmosphere of the planets Mars and Venus today. The steam **condensed** to form the early oceans.

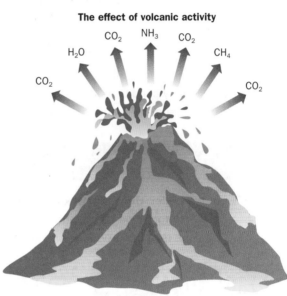

The effect of volcanic activity

Later

During the two billion years that followed, **plants** and **algae** evolved and began to cover the surface of the Earth.

> **KEY POINT**
>
> The plants grew very well in the carbon dioxide-rich atmosphere. They steadily removed carbon dioxide and produced oxygen (O_2).

Later still

Most of the carbon dioxide in the early atmosphere dissolved into the oceans. The carbon gradually became locked up in the shells and skeletons of marine organisms and, when the organisms died, as **carbonate** minerals. Some of the carbon from the early atmosphere is also stored in fossil fuels. The ammonia in the early atmosphere reacted with oxygen to release nitrogen. Living organisms, such as denitrifying bacteria, also produced nitrogen. As the amount of oxygen increased, an **ozone layer** (O_3) developed. This layer filtered out harmful **ultraviolet (UV) radiation** from the Sun, enabling new, more complex life forms to develop.

> Remember that it is difficult for scientists to be completely precise about all the details above because different sources of information suggest slightly different things may have happened.

Chemical theories for the origins of life

AQA	C1	✓
EDEXCEL	C1	✓

Historically, people believed that life started when living things were spontaneously generated from non-living materials. These ideas are part of the teaching of many religions. Today, many scientists believe that life started because of chemical reactions taking place, possibly between hydrocarbons, ammonia and lightning. The Earth's early environment would have provided the necessary conditions and raw materials (or **primordial soup**) for life to develop. There are many theories about how life first evolved.

Miller–Urey experiment

AQA	C1	✓

In the **Miller–Urey experiment**, water, methane, ammonia and hydrogen were placed into sterile flasks and exposed to electrical sparks. Miller and Urey found that the reaction produced amino acids.

Carbon dioxide in the atmosphere

AQA	C1	✓
OCR A	C1	✓
OCR B	C1	✓
EDEXCEL	C1	✓
WJEC	C1	✓
CCEA	C2	✓

> **KEY POINT**
>
> The level of carbon dioxide in our atmosphere has increased since the **Industrial Revolution** as we have burned more fossil fuels.

These fossil fuels had stored carbon from the Earth's early atmosphere for hundreds of millions of years.

There is a mismatch, however, between the amount of carbon dioxide released into the atmosphere by the burning of fossil fuels and the actual increase in the amount of carbon dioxide in the atmosphere. A great deal of the carbon dioxide appears to be missing.

Carbon dioxide is removed from the atmosphere by:

- **photosynthesis** by plants on land
- photosynthesis by phytoplankton in the oceans
- dissolution of carbon dioxide molecules from the atmosphere to the oceans.

The carbon dioxide reacts with seawater to produce:

- **insoluble** (does not dissolve) carbonate salts, which are deposited as sediment
- **soluble** (does dissolve) calcium and magnesium hydrogencarbonate salts.

Much of the carbon dioxide is, therefore, locked up in sediment for long periods of time. Some of this carbon dioxide is later released back into the atmosphere when the sediment is forced underground by geological activity and then released when volcanoes erupt.

However, not all of the carbon dioxide released by the burning of fossil fuels is removed in these ways. Many people are concerned about rising levels of carbon dioxide in the Earth's atmosphere and the possible link between these increased levels and **global warming**. The theories about the evolution of the Earth's atmosphere come from scientific studies of rocks formed millions of years ago. Scientists' ideas evolve as more evidence becomes available.

PROGRESS CHECK

1. Approximately how much of today's atmosphere is made up of oxygen?
2. What was the main gas in the Earth's early atmosphere?
3. How did the evolution of plants affect the Earth's atmosphere?
4. What happened to most of the carbon from the carbon dioxide in the Earth's early atmosphere?
5. What does the ozone layer do?
6. Describe the experiment carried out by Miller and Urey and explain why the results of the experiment were so significant.

6. Water, methane, ammonia and hydrogen were placed into sterile flasks and exposed to electrical sparks. These reactions produced amino acids. This showed that chemical reactions could produce the building blocks of life.
5. It filters out harmful UV rays.
4. It became locked up in sedimentary rocks and fossil fuels.
3. It removed carbon dioxide and produced oxygen.
2. Carbon dioxide.
1. 21%

2.2 Noble gases and the fractional distillation of air

LEARNING SUMMARY

After studying this section, you should be able to:

- Recall the percentage composition of air.
- Describe an experiment to show that air is 20% oxygen.
- Understand the separation of air by fractional distillation.
- Explain the low reactivity of the noble gases.
- List some uses of noble gases.

The level of oxygen present in air

AQA	C1	✓
OCR A	C5	✓
OCR B	C1	✓
EDEXCEL	C1, C2	✓
WJEC	C1	✓

Air is a mixture of different gases. About 78% of air is **nitrogen**, about 21% is **oxygen** and about 1% is a mixture of **other gases** including argon, neon, water vapour and carbon dioxide. All of these molecules and atoms are very small. There are large spaces between them. Nitrogen is an element. Nitrogen exists as molecules, with the formula N_2. Oxygen is also an element and exists as molecules, with the formula O_2. Argon and neon are both elements that exist as single atoms. They are represented by the symbols Ar and Ne.

> Learn the percentage of nitrogen and oxygen in the air and be prepared to recall the information in the exam. Nitrogen and oxygen are both diatomic molecules. A diatomic molecule consists of two atoms joined together.

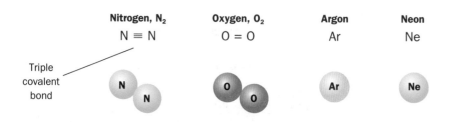

Water vapour is a molecular compound, with the formula H_2O. Carbon dioxide is also a molecular compound, with the formula CO_2.

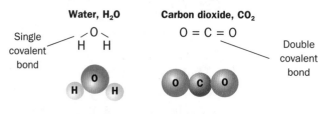

Combustion reactions

OCR A	C1	✓
OCR B	C1	✓
EDEXCEL	C1, C2	✓
WJEC	C3	✓
CCEA	C2	✓

Combustion, or burning reactions, needs oxygen. In fact, fuels will burn better in pure oxygen than they do in air. Oxygen can be mixed with the fuel acetylene in welding torches.

Combustion

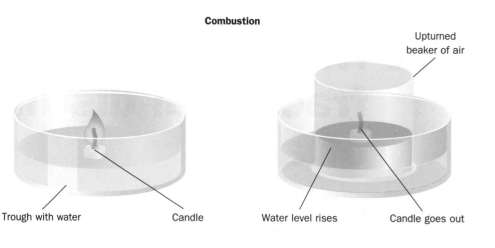

If an upturned beaker is placed over a candle, the oxygen in the air is used up as the candle burns and the water level inside the beaker moves up. When the candle uses up all the oxygen in the air the candle goes out. The water level moves about a fifth of the way up the beaker. This shows that about a fifth, or around 20%, of the air is oxygen.

Fractional distillation of liquid air

| AQA | C1 | ✓ |
| EDEXCEL | C2 | ✓ |

Fractional distillation separates mixtures into different fractions, or parts, because the fractions have different boiling points. Both oxygen and nitrogen can be extracted from air by fractional distillation.

First, the air is filtered to remove dust and other impurities. Next, the air is cooled until it reaches −200°C. The gases condense to form liquids. Carbon dioxide and water are removed as they condense, leaving a mixture of liquid nitrogen and oxygen. Oxygen turns from a liquid to a gas at −183°C, while nitrogen turns from a liquid to a gas at −196°C. The **liquefied** air mixture is placed into a **fractionating column**.

Separating oxygen and nitrogen

The nitrogen boils and is collected at the top of the column.

Cooler

Mixture containing liquid oxygen and nitrogen at −200°C

Warmer

The liquid oxygen is collected at the bottom.

> Design a flow diagram to show each step in the fractional distillation of air.

A final step is required to remove traces of argon from the oxygen. These two gases have such similar boiling points that a second fractional distillation step is required to separate them. The gases separated from air are useful raw materials that are used in many industrial processes.

Noble gases

AQA	C1	✓
EDEXCEL	C2	✓
WJEC	C1	✓
CCEA	C1	✓

KEY POINT

The elements of group 0 are called the **noble gases**. Noble gases are very **unreactive**. They are sometimes described as being **inert** because they do not react. This is because they have a full, stable outer shell of electrons.

A model showing outer shell of electrons of the noble gases

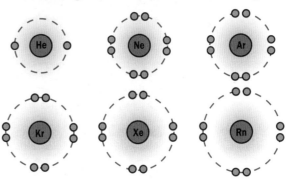

Notice that the noble gases have eight electrons in their outer shell, except helium. Helium only has two electrons but that still gives it a full outer shell.

Noble gases are useful to us precisely because they do not react. They are inert, have a **low density** and are **non-flammable**. The table shows some uses of noble gases.

Gas	Use	Image
Helium	Used in balloons and in airships because it is less dense than air. It is not flammable. (Early airships used hydrogen, which is flammable, and this could be disastrous if a fault occurred and the hydrogen caught fire.)	
Neon	Used in electrical discharge tubes in advertising signs.	
Argon	Used in filament light bulbs. The hot filament is surrounded by argon. This stops the filament from burning away and breaking the bulb.	

PROGRESS CHECK

1. What percentage of the air is nitrogen?
2. What is the formula of carbon dioxide?
3. Why can liquid air be separated by fractional distillation?
4. How many electrons does a helium atom have?
5. Outline the steps involved in the fractional distillation of air.
6. Why is it better to use helium than hydrogen in balloons?

1. 78%.
2. CO_2.
3. The different components have different boiling points.
4. 2 electrons.
5. First the air is filtered then it is cooled. The gases condense to form liquids. Carbon dioxide and water are removed as they condense leaving a mixture of liquid nitrogen and oxygen, which are separated by fractional distillation. Oxygen turns from a liquid to a gas at −183°C, while nitrogen turns from a liquid to a gas at −196°C. A second fractional distillation step is required to remove traces of argon from the oxygen.
6. Hydrogen is a flammable gas while helium, which also has a low density, is extremely unreactive and so much safer.

2.3 Pollution of the atmosphere

After studying this section, you should be able to:

LEARNING SUMMARY

- List the fossil fuels burned to provide energy.
- Write balanced equations for the combustion of hydrocarbons.
- Explain how sulfur impurities cause acid rain.
- Understand why limiting oxygen supply can produce carbon monoxide.
- Describe how a catalytic converter removes pollutants from car exhaust fumes.

Fossil fuels

AQA	C1	✓
OCR A	C1	✓
OCR B	C1	✓
EDEXCEL	C1	✓
WJEC	C1	✓
CCEA	C2	✓

Coal is mainly carbon. Petrol, diesel, oil and natural gas are **hydrocarbons**. When hydrocarbons are burned in a good supply of oxygen, water vapour and carbon dioxide are produced. The carbon and hydrogen atoms in the hydrocarbon fuels combine with oxygen atoms. This is an example of an **oxidation** reaction.

Practise writing balanced symbol equations for combustion of fuels.

methane + oxygen → carbon dioxide + water vapour

$$CH_4 + 2O_2 \rightarrow CO_2 + 2H_2O$$

Fuels will burn more quickly in pure oxygen than they will in air. The products made in these reactions can be **pollutants** that affect air quality.

Acid rain

AQA	C1	✓
OCR A	C1	✓
OCR B	C1	✓
EDEXCEL	C1	✓
WJEC	C1	✓
CCEA	C2	✓

KEY POINT

Fossil fuels, such as coal, oil and gas, often contain small amounts of sulfur. When these fuels are burned, the gas sulfur dioxide, SO_2, is produced. This gas can dissolve in rainwater to form **acid rain**.

Acid rain can affect the environment by damaging statues and buildings, as well as harming plant and aquatic life and corroding metals.

The damaging effect of acid rain on plant life

Fossil fuels are burned in power stations to produce electricity. Using less electricity, by turning off lights when they are not in use and not leaving everyday appliances on standby mode, will help to reduce the amount of acid rain produced.

Removing sulfur

OCR A	C1	✓
EDEXCEL	C1	✓
WJEC	C1	✓
CCEA	C2	✓

Remember, sulfur dioxide causes acid rain. You could be asked to recall the chemical responsible for this environmental problem.

Alternatively, sulfur compounds can be removed directly from oil and gas before they are burned so that they do not produce sulfur dioxide as they burn. The sulfur that is removed is a valuable material that can be sold on.

It is more difficult to remove sulfur from the fossil fuel coal. However, the sulfur dioxide produced by burning coal can be removed from the waste gases before they are released into the atmosphere. This process is carried out by scrubbers in power stations. The scrubbers react sulfur dioxide (from the waste gases) with calcium carbonate to produce gypsum and carbon dioxide. Sulfur dioxide can also be removed by oxidation and reaction with ammonia or by using seawater.

Carbon monoxide

OCR A	C1	✓
OCR B	C1	✓
EDEXCEL	C1	✓
CCEA	C2	✓

The gas carbon monoxide, or CO, can be a dangerous pollutant. When fossil fuels containing carbon and hydrogen are burned, carbon dioxide and water vapour are produced. However, if carbon is burned in an **insufficient** supply of oxygen, the gas carbon monoxide can also be produced. Carbon monoxide is colourless, odourless and very poisonous. Faulty gas appliances can produce carbon monoxide, so it is important that they are regularly serviced. **Incomplete combustion** is undesirable because:

- It produces carbon monoxide.
- Less heat than expected is given off when the fuel is burned.
- Soot is produced, which must then be cleaned. A sooty flame has a yellow colour.

Global dimming is caused by smoke particles that are released into the atmosphere. Scientists believe that these smoke particles reduce the amount of sunlight that reaches the Earth's surface and may even affect weather patterns.

Catalytic converters

OCR A	C1	✓
OCR B	C1	✓
EDEXCEL	C2	✓

In the UK, modern, petrol-fuelled cars are fitted with **catalytic converters** or 'cats'. The catalytic converter is part of a car's exhaust system and helps to reduce the amount of harmful gases that the car releases into the atmosphere. Catalytic converters work best at high temperatures and have a high surface area to increase the rate at which harmful gases are converted.

Catalytic converters work in several ways:

- They help to convert carbon monoxide to carbon dioxide. The carbon monoxide is oxidised and the nitrogen monoxide is reduced.

  $$2CO + 2NO \rightarrow N_2 + 2CO_2$$

- They help to convert nitrogen oxides to nitrogen.
- They oxidise unburned hydrocarbons to carbon dioxide and water vapour.

Nitrogen oxide is produced when nitrogen from air reacts with oxygen from air at the high temperatures reached when fuels are burned inside internal combustion engines. The nitrogen oxide reacts with oxygen to form nitrogen dioxide. Nitrogen oxide and nitrogen dioxide are referred to as nitrogen oxides or NOx. Nitrogen oxides cause acid rain and photochemical smog.

Atmospheric pollution caused by cars can also be reduced by:

- having more efficient car engines
- encouraging people to make more use of public transport
- setting legal limits for the levels of pollutants in exhaust gases (these levels are checked during MOT tests).

> **Design a spider diagram to show how the amount of pollution produced by cars can be reduced.**

PROGRESS CHECK

1. What is the name of the gas produced when sulfur is burned?
2. How can you tell from the flame that a fuel is being burned in a poor supply of oxygen?
3. What gas is produced when carbon is burned in a good supply of oxygen?
4. What gas is produced when carbon is burned in an insufficient supply of oxygen?
5. What causes global dimming?
6. Use a balanced symbol equation to show how a catalytic converter can help to remove carbon monoxide and nitrogen oxide from the exhaust gases of a car.

6. $2CO + 2NO \rightarrow N_2 + 2CO_2$.
5. Smoke particles.
4. Carbon monoxide.
3. Carbon dioxide.
2. It will have a yellow colour.
1. Sulfur dioxide.

2.4 The greenhouse effect and ozone depletion

LEARNING SUMMARY

After studying this section, you should be able to:

- Explain what is meant by 'the greenhouse effect'.
- Recall examples of ways to reduce atmospheric carbon dioxide.
- Understand the role of ozone in filtering out harmful ultraviolet rays.
- Give examples of alternatives to CFCs that do not damage ozone.

Carbon dioxide and the greenhouse effect

OCR B	C1, C6	✓
EDEXCEL	C1	✓
WJEC	C1	✓
CCEA	C2	✓

> Remember that the levels of carbon dioxide in the atmosphere are rising as more fossil fuels are burned.

The **greenhouse effect** is believed to be slowly heating up the Earth. When fossil fuels are burned, the gas carbon dioxide is produced. Although some of this carbon dioxide is removed from the atmosphere by the reaction between carbon dioxide and seawater, the overall amount of carbon dioxide in the atmosphere has increased over the last 200 years.

KEY POINT

Carbon dioxide traps the heat energy that has reached the Earth from the Sun.

Global warming may mean that the polar ice caps will eventually melt and this could cause massive flooding.

The greenhouse effect

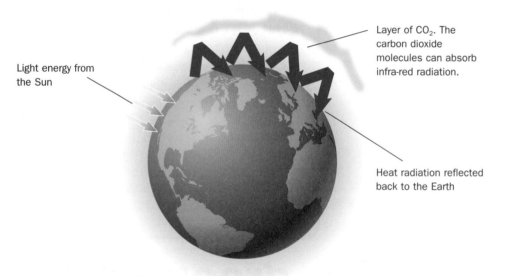

Light energy from the Sun

Layer of CO_2. The carbon dioxide molecules can absorb infra-red radiation.

Heat radiation reflected back to the Earth

Plants use the gas carbon dioxide during photosynthesis so **deforestation** reduces the amount of carbon dioxide that can be removed from the air. Organisms release carbon dioxide during respiration. Methane and water vapour are also greenhouse gases.

Reducing carbon dioxide levels

OCR B	C1	✓
EDEXCEL	C1	✓
WJEC	C1	✓

In **carbon capture and storage**, the carbon dioxide produced by power stations is captured and then stored safely. The carbon dioxide can be stored in **porous** rocks. Carbon dioxide can also be converted into **carbonate** rocks and then stored.

Not all scientists believe that human activity is causing global warming. Other factors, such as solar cycles, may also be important. Scientists are also investigating ways to control the amount of carbon dioxide by:

- adding iron to the oceans to encourage algae to **photosynthesise**
- converting carbon dioxide into useful hydrocarbons.

Ozone

OCR B   C6   ✓

Chlorofluorocarbons (CFCs) are organic molecules that contain carbon, chlorine and fluorine atoms. They:

- are chemically inert and, therefore, non-toxic
- have low boiling points
- do not dissolve in water.

In the past, CFCs were widely used as aerosol propellants, as coolants in refrigerators and freezers and solvents used in dry-cleaning. Scientists believed the chemicals were safe to use. Then they found a link between CFCs and the depletion of the ozone layer. Scientists discovered that the ozone layer was being damaged and they persuaded the rest of the world community that CFCs were responsible and should be replaced. They also worked hard to find replacements.

Ozone, O_3, molecules consist of three oxygen atoms. The ozone layer is part of the stratosphere, which is in the Earth's atmosphere.

Images showing the developing hole in the ozone layer

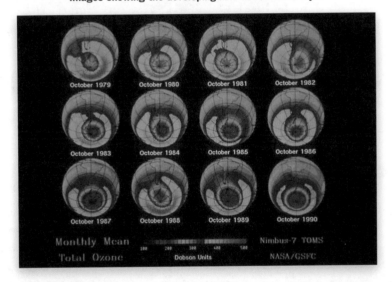

KEY POINT

Ozone in the stratosphere is important because it filters out harmful **ultraviolet (UV) radiation** and prevents it from reaching the lower part of the atmosphere.

If more UV light reaches the lower part of the atmosphere, people could suffer medical problems including:

> Do not just state that UV causes cancer. You need to be clear that UV causes skin cancer.

- an increased risk of sunburn
- skin being damaged and aged more quickly
- more cases of skin cancers
- development of more **cataracts**.

CFCs have been banned from use in almost all new products, but old fridges and freezers produced before the ban will still contain CFC molecules. When these fridges and freezers stop working, the CFCs must be removed to stop them from escaping into the atmosphere.

CFC molecules are stable because the carbon-hydrogen bonds are very strong and hard to break. However, CFC molecules do break down slowly in the Earth's stratosphere. UV light breaks down the strong covalent bonds in the CFC molecules.

Alternatives to CFCs

OCR B C6 ✓

Scientists have developed alternative compounds that can be used in place of CFCs, and do much less damage to the ozone layer.

Hydrofluorocarbons, or HCFCs, have now widely replaced CFCs. HCFCs are non-toxic and non-flammable but they are very potent greenhouse gases.

> **PROGRESS CHECK**
>
> 1 How does adding iron to oceans reduce levels of carbon dioxide?
> 2 What do the initials CFC stand for?
> 3 How were CFCs used?
>
> 1. It encourages algae to photosynthesise.
> 2. Chlorofluorocarbons.
> 3. Aerosol propellants, coolants and as solvents.

2.5 Pollution of the environment

LEARNING SUMMARY

After studying this section, you should be able to:

- Describe the problems caused by over-use of nitrate fertilisers.
- Explain why crude oil spills cause damage to the environment.
- Understand the environmental impact of quarrying bauxite and limestone.
- Describe the problems associated with the disposal of plastics.
- Understand what is meant by the 'Life cycle assessment' of an object.

Pollution

OCR B C1 ✓
WJEC C1, C3 ✓

All substances are made from matter obtained from the Earth's crust, the sea or the atmosphere. It is vital that we protect the environment from harmful **pollution**. Some chemicals persist for long periods of time in the environment. Such chemicals can be carried over large distances and may even accumulate in human tissues because of food consumption. Today, there are a large number of chemicals in the environment that may adversely affect the environment or human health, but scientists do not have enough data yet to be sure of all their effects.

Pollution is not always as obvious as this!

Problems with nitrate fertilisers

OCR A	C7	✓
OCR B	C2	✓
EDEXCEL	C3	✓
WJEC	C3	✓
CCEA	C2	✓

Nitrogen, potassium and phosphorus are all needed for plants to grow. Nitrate **fertilisers** help plants to grow well and this means that farmers are able to produce more food. Nitrate fertilisers can cause problems if they are washed into lakes or streams:

- Algae (small plants) thrive in the fertiliser-rich water and grow very well.
- Eventually, the algae die and bacteria start to decompose (break down) the algae.
- As the bacteria decompose the algae, they use up the oxygen in the water.
- Fish and other aquatic life cannot get enough oxygen, so they die.

This process is called **eutrophication**.

Nitrate fertilisers can also find their way into drinking water supplies. There have been health concerns over the levels of nitrates in water and the prevalence of stomach cancer and 'blue baby' disease. Babies suffering from blue baby disease have elevated levels of nitrates in their blood. These nitrates reduce the amount of oxygen that the blood can carry, so the baby's skin looks blue. Although no firm links have yet been proved, it seems sensible to limit the levels of nitrate in drinking water until more is known.

Problems with oil exploitation

OCR B	C1	✓
EDEXCEL	C1	✓
CCEA	C2	✓

Oil is an extremely important raw material. It is found in porous rocks in the Earth's crust. Sometimes, the crude oil has to be pumped up to the surface before it can be collected. It is often transported around the world in giant oil tankers. When accidents occasionally occur, crude oil can escape. The oil forms a slick that can devastate animal and plant life. For example, sea birds can die if their feathers become covered in oil. These oil slicks can do great damage to affected beaches; this can have serious consequences for local people, particularly in holiday areas. If detergents are used to break up the oil slicks, the **detergents** may also affect wildlife.

In addition to the environmental problems associated with the exploitation of crude oil, there are also political problems that must be considered. Oil reserves are often found in politically sensitive areas. These countries may not want to sell great quantities of oil as a shortage in the world supply will naturally lead to an increase in the price of the oil. In other areas the situation can be even more unstable: battles in areas around oil fields can make it too dangerous for the oil to be extracted safely.

Problems with bauxite quarrying

OCR A	C5	✓
EDEXCEL	C1	✓
CCEA	C2	✓

Aluminium is extracted from its ore, **bauxite**. Unfortunately, this ore is often found in environmentally sensitive areas such as the Amazonian rainforest.

Bauxite is extracted from large opencast mines. Large numbers of trees must be cut down to clear space for the mine and new roads built to give access to the mine. In addition, litter and oil can pollute the area around the mine.

An opencast mine

However, aluminium can be recycled, which can cut down on landfill in the UK and help to preserve the Amazonian rainforests.

Problems with limestone quarrying

AQA	C1	✓
OCR A	C2	✓
EDEXCEL	C1	✓
WJEC	C3	✓
CCEA	C2	✓

Make sure you can recall some of the advantages and disadvantages of limestone quarrying.

Limestone is a very important raw material. The economic benefits of quarrying for limestone must be balanced against the social and environmental consequences of quarrying. Limestone has to be blasted from hillsides in huge quantities. This scars the landscape, causes noise pollution and dust, and affects local wildlife. Transporting limestone from the quarry can also cause problems, with heavy lorries causing noise, congestion and damaging local roads. Quarrying does, however, create new jobs and brings new money into an area.

Plastics

AQA	C1	✓
OCR A	C2	✓
OCR B	C1	✓
EDEXCEL	C1	✓
WJEC	C1	✓
CCEA	C2	✓

Plastics are very useful materials:

- They are very stable and unreactive, and waterproof.
- Most plastics do not react with water, oxygen or other common chemicals.
- Plastics are also non-biodegradable, which means that they are not decomposed by microorganisms.

> **KEY POINT**
>
> When plastic objects are no longer needed, they do not rot away but remain in the environment. Plastic objects now fill many landfill sites.

Plastics can be disposed of by burning, but this solution may also cause pollution problems. Although some plastics burn quite easily, they can give off harmful gases. The common plastic PVC releases the gas hydrogen chloride when it is burned. The plasticisers added to PVC sometimes leach out of the plastics and have harmful effects in the environment.

In response to these problems, scientists have developed new, biodegradable plastics that will eventually rot away. Some biodegradable plastics have been made from corn starch and some can be disposed of by dissolving them in water.

Glass and plastic bottles can be recycled but they can also be reused to store other liquids.

In addition, scientists are developing ways to recycle plastics. Polyesters, which can be used to make fabrics and bottles, can be recycled to form fleece material to make new clothes. Currently, recycling plastics is difficult because the different types of polymer have to be sorted by hand, and this is very expensive. **Recycling** also means that our finite resources of crude oil will last longer.

Life cycle assessment (LCA)

| OCR A | C3 | ✓ |

Life cycle assessment (LCA) is used to assess the environmental impact an object has over its whole lifetime. This is sometimes referred to as **from cradle to grave**. LCAs are an effective way of comparing several possible alternative products to see which one has the least impact on the environment.

To calculate the overall effect, scientists measure the impact of:

- extracting the raw materials
- the manufacturing process
- any packaging used
- how the product is transported
- how it is used
- what happens to the object when it is no longer useful.

Recycling an object, if possible, will reduce its adverse effect on the environment.

PROGRESS CHECK

1. Name the main ore of aluminium.
2. How is crude oil transported around the world?
3. How can limestone extraction affect the landscape?
4. What are the advantages of a new, local limestone quarry?
5. What does the term 'non-biodegradable' mean?
6. Explain how recycling aluminium objects will help to preserve Amazonian rainforests.

1. Bauxite.
2. Using oil tankers.
3. The quarries can scar the landscape.
4. It brings new jobs and brings money into the area.
5. It is not decomposed by microorganisms.
6. Aluminium is extracted from its ore, bauxite. Deposits of bauxite are found in these rainforests. If we recycle our existing aluminium objects then less fresh aluminium will be required so less bauxite will need to be quarried.

2.6 Evidence of plate tectonics

LEARNING SUMMARY

After studying this section, you should be able to:

- Describe the structure of the Earth and its composition.
- Understand the evidence that has led to this model of Earth's structure.
- Explain the movement of tectonic plates floating on the liquid mantle.
- Recall that Alfred Wegener originally proposed his theory of 'continental drift'.
- Describe the evidence supporting Wegener's theory.

The structure of the Earth

AQA	C1	✓
OCR A	C5	✓
OCR B	C2	✓
WJEC	C1	✓
CCEA	C2	✓

Scientists believe that the Earth has a layered structure. The outer layer, called the **crust**, is very thin and has a low **density**. The next layer down is called the **mantle**. This layer extends almost halfway to the centre of the Earth. The rock in the mantle is mainly solid, but small amounts must be liquid as the mantle flows very slowly. At the centre of the Earth is the **core**. The core consists of

Make sure you can recall the names and details of the different layers of the Earth.

two parts: the outer core is liquid; the inner core, which is under even greater pressure, is solid.

The layered structure of the Earth

Crust: The crust is the outermost layer of the Earth, and is rich in silicon, oxygen and aluminium. Much of the silicon and oxygen in the Earth's crust is present as silicon dioxide or silica.

Core: The core lies at the centre of the Earth. It is thought to be made of iron and nickel.

Mantle: The mantle is found between the crust and the core and is partially liquid. Rocks in the mantle flow slowly.

Continental crust: The continental crust consists of sedimentary rock, igneous rock and metamorphic rock. The igneous rock found in the continental crust is mainly granite.

Oceanic crust: The oceanic crust consists mainly of basalt.

Evidence of the structure of the Earth

OCR B	C2	✓
WJEC	C1	✓
CCEA	C2	✓

The Earth's crust is too thick to drill through so evidence for the layered structure of the Earth comes from studies of the way that **seismic waves** (the shock waves sent out by earthquakes) travel through the Earth.

The material through which the shock waves travel affects the speed of these waves. These studies show that the outer core of the Earth is liquid while the inner core is solid. The overall **density** of the Earth is greater than the density of the rocks that make up the Earth's crust. This means that the rocks in the mantle and the core must be much denser than the rocks we observe in the crust. Scientists believe that the core is mainly made of iron and nickel.

Movement of the crust

AQA	C1	✓
OCR A	C3	✓
OCR B	C2	✓
WJEC	C1	✓
CCEA	C2	✓

People used to believe that the features of the Earth's surface, such as the mountain ranges, were formed when the surface of the Earth shrank as it cooled down. However, scientists now believe that the Earth's geological features can be explained using a single, unifying theory called **plate tectonics**.

> **KEY POINT**
>
> In 1914, the scientist Alfred Wegener first proposed **continental drift**, the idea behind plate tectonics. Initially, these ideas were resisted, particularly by religious groups. Scientists examining Wegener's theory could not, at first, explain how or why the plates moved, but as more evidence emerged, the theory of plate tectonics was gradually accepted.

Plate movement

AQA	C1	✓
OCR A	C3	✓
OCR B	C2	✓
WJEC	C1	✓
CCEA	C2	

The main idea behind plate tectonics is that the Earth's **lithosphere** (the crust and upper mantle) is split up into 12 large **plates**. Each plate moves slowly over the Earth's surface at a rate of a few centimetres each year. The movement of the plates is caused by convection currents in the mantle. These currents are caused by the natural **radioactive** decay of elements deep inside the Earth that release heat energy. By studying geological processes, scientists have been able to explain what has happened in the past. These scientists believe that at one time all the continents were joined together to form a **supercontinent** called **Pangea**. Since that time, the continents have moved apart and are now at their maximum separation.

How the continents once looked

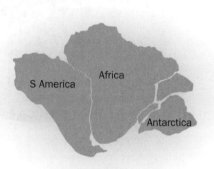

Evidence to support the theory

AQA	C1	✓
OCR A	C3	✓
OCR B	C2	✓
WJEC	C1	✓
CCEA	C2	✓

There are many clues that support our ideas about plate tectonics:

- When the South American coast was first mapped, people noticed that the east coast of South America and the west coast of Africa fitted together like pieces of an enormous jigsaw.

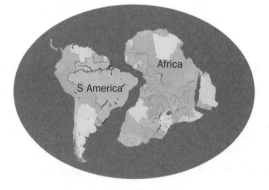

- The examination of fossil remains in both South America and Africa showed that rocks of the same age contained the remains of an unusual freshwater crocodile-type creature.
- Further evidence that South America and Africa were once joined was uncovered when scientists discovered that rock strata of the same age were strikingly similar on both sides of the Atlantic.

Strata layers in British sedimentary rocks

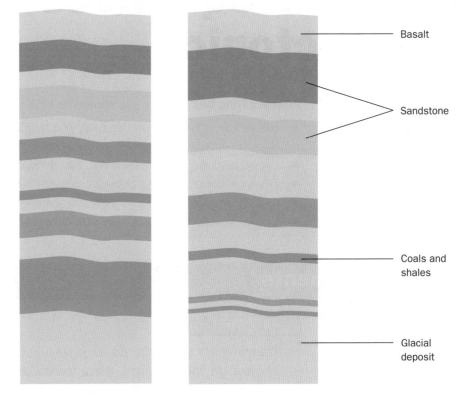

- Basalt
- Sandstone
- Coals and shales
- Glacial deposit

> Learn what the Earth's lithosphere is made up of.

- British rocks that were created in the **Carboniferous period** (300 million years ago) must have formed in tropical swamps. Yet rocks found in Britain, which formed 200 million years ago, must have formed in deserts. This shows that Britain must have moved through different climatic zones as the tectonic plate that Britain rests on moved across the Earth's surface.

Ideas about plate tectonics have changed over time. Scientists build a model that fits with the evidence currently available to them. When new evidence is discovered they must re-evaluate their existing models and, if necessary, change them to take in the new evidence.

PROGRESS CHECK

1. What name is given to the outer layer of the Earth?
2. In which state is the Earth's inner core?
3. Which elements are abundant in the Earth's crust?
4. Which elements are abundant in the Earth's core?
5. Where does our evidence for the structure of the Earth come from?
6. What is the Earth's lithosphere?
7. Describe why the Earth's plates move.

1. The crust.
2. Solid.
3. Silicon, oxygen and aluminium.
4. Iron and nickel.
5. It comes from the study of seismic waves.
6. The crust and upper mantle.
7. The Earth's lithosphere (crust and upper mantle) is split up into about a dozen large plates. Each of these plates moves slowly over the Earth's surface. The movement of the plates is caused by convection currents in the mantle. These currents are caused by the natural radioactive decay of elements deep inside the Earth, which release heat energy.

2.7 Consequences of plate tectonics

LEARNING SUMMARY

After studying this section, you should be able to:

- Recall that volcanoes, earthquakes and tsunamis are caused by events at plate boundaries.
- Understand why these events are very difficult to predict.
- Describe the differences between different types of lava.
- Explain how mountain ranges are formed when plates converge.
- Explain how mid-oceanic ridges are formed when plates move apart.

Plate movements

AQA	C1	✓
OCR B	C2	✓
WJEC	C1	✓
CCEA	C2	✓

> **KEY POINT**
>
> The movement of tectonic plates causes many problems, including earthquakes and volcanoes. These tend to be worse near the edges of plates, known as the plate boundaries.

> In exam questions you may be asked to select an answer to indicate how fast tectonic plates move. Remember, the plates move very slowly – about the same speed as your fingernails grow.

The plates can move in three different ways:

1. They can slide past or over each other.
2. They can move towards each other.
3. They can move away from each other.

These diagrams show how the Earth's plates can move.

Earthquakes

AQA	C1	✓
OCR B	C2	✓
WJEC	C1	✓
CCEA	C2	✓

Earthquakes are caused by tectonic plates sliding past or over each other. The San Andreas Fault in California is a famous example of where this occurs.

The San Andreas Fault

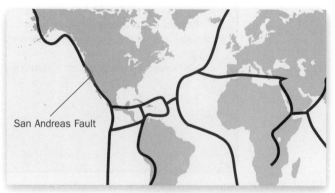

San Andreas Fault

The plates in this area have fractured into a very complicated pattern. As the plates try to move past each other, they tend to stick together rather than slide smoothly past. When the plates stick together, forces build up until eventually the plates suddenly move. The strain that has built up is released in the form of an earthquake. If this happens beneath the oceans, it can result in catastrophic tsunami waves.

> **KEY POINT**
>
> Scientists have studied earthquakes in an effort to predict when they will occur and so warn people to move away from the affected areas. However, with so many factors involved, it is not always possible to predict exactly when an earthquake or a volcanic eruption will happen.

When they do happen, they can cause massive destruction and loss of life.

The results of an earthquake

> Scientists do not know exactly when earthquakes will occur because they do not fully understand the processes happening below the Earth's crust.

Volcanoes

AQA	C1	✓
OCR B	C2	✓
WJEC	C1	✓
CCEA	C2	✓

Like earthquakes, volcanoes are sometimes found in locations around the Earth where two plates are moving towards each other. By studying where most earthquakes and volcanoes happen, scientists have been able to identify plate boundaries.

These convergent plate boundaries often involve the collision between an oceanic and a continental plate. Oceanic plates contain minerals that are rich in the elements iron and magnesium, and are denser than continental plates. When an oceanic plate and a continental plate converge, the denser, oceanic plate is forced beneath the continental plate. The continental plate is stressed, and the existing rocks are folded and metamorphosed.

Diagram showing a convergent plate boundary

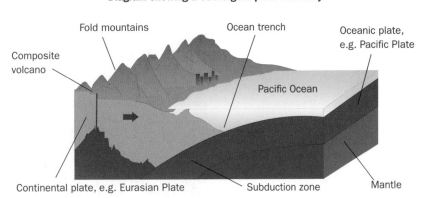

As the oceanic plate is forced down beneath the continental plate, seawater lowers the melting point of the rock and some of the oceanic plate may melt to form magma. If the magma has a lower density than the surrounding rock in the Earth's crust it can rise up through weaknesses or cracks in the crust to form volcanoes. Magma is molten rock below the Earth's surface; it becomes lava as it reaches the Earth's surface. Lava erupts from volcanoes. Some iron-rich basaltic lavas are runny and are relatively safe. Elsewhere, silica-rich viscous lavas are produced. These lavas are much more dangerous: they explode violently, often producing pumice, clouds of choking ash and throwing out pieces of rock called bombs. Volcanoes that erupt this way are much more dangerous.

When the lava cools down and solidifies, it forms igneous rocks. The faster the lava cools down the smaller the crystals in the rock will be. Some people choose to live near to volcanoes, even though they might erupt, because the soils formed when the igneous rocks are weathered are very fertile.

As the plates are moving past each other, earthquakes are also common in these areas.

A convergent plate boundary along the Western coast of South America is responsible for the formation of the Andes mountain range.

Diagram showing the Earth's plate boundaries

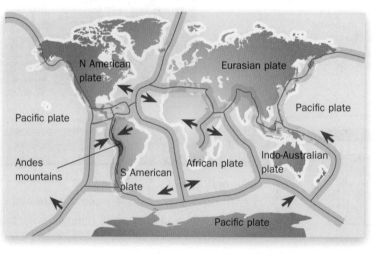

Mid-ocean ridge basalts

OCR B   C2   ✓

Another consequence of plate tectonics is the formation of mid-ocean ridge basalts.

Diagram showing a divergent plate boundary

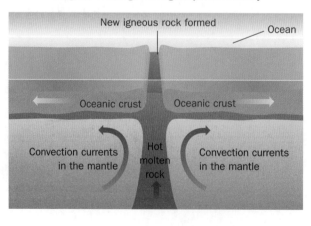

When tectonic plates move apart, magma comes to the surface. This usually occurs under oceans. As the molten rock cools, it solidifies and forms the igneous rock, basalt. These plate boundaries are often referred to as constructive plate boundaries, because new crust is being made. Basalt is rich in iron, which is magnetic. As the basalt cools down, the iron-rich minerals in the basalt line up with the Earth's magnetic field. By examining the direction in which these minerals have lined up, scientists in the 1960s discovered that they were able to work out the direction of the Earth's magnetic field. However, examination of the basalt rocks on either side of a mid-ocean ridge shows a striped magnetic reversal pattern. The pattern is symmetrical about the ridge and provides evidence that the Earth's magnetic field periodically changes direction. This reversal appears to be very sudden and occurs about every half a million years. According to the rock record, another reversal is now well overdue!

PROGRESS CHECK

1. What causes earthquakes?
2. Why can't scientists predict the exact date of an earthquake?
3. Why do earthquakes sometimes occur near volcanoes?
4. Why do oceanic plates move below continental plates when they collide?
5. Where is the Andes mountain range?
6. Explain how magnetic reversal patterns are formed near ocean ridges.

1. Earthquakes are caused when plates suddenly move past or over each other, having been restricted and causing stress to build up. The sudden release of this stress results in an earthquake.
2. There are too many factors involved.
3. Earthquakes sometimes occur near volcanoes because plates are moving past or over each other, having been restricted and causing stress to build up. The sudden release of this stress results in an earthquake.
4. The oceanic plates are denser.
5. The Western coast of South America.
6. When the Earth's magnetic field reverses, the iron minerals in the solidifying lava line up with the Earth's magnetic field in the new opposite direction, forming a symmetrical pattern about the ridge.

2.8 Everyday chemistry

LEARNING SUMMARY

After studying this section, you should be able to:

- Explain why cooking food is an example of a chemical reaction.
- Describe the changes in protein molecules when they are cooked.
- Understand the meaning of the term 'colloid'.
- List the components of a typical paint.
- Understand how washing-up liquids help clean plates and cutlery.

Cooking

OCR B   C1   ✓

During a **chemical reaction**, a new substance is made in an **irreversible** process and there is an **energy change**. Cooking food is an example of a chemical reaction. Eggs and meat are examples of **proteins** needed by the body for growth and repair. When cooked, their appearance and texture changes. Potatoes are a source of **carbohydrate**. When they are cooked, they become softer and fluffier and their taste improves.

When eggs or meat are cooked, the protein molecules change shape; this irreversible process is called **denaturing**. When potatoes are cooked the starch grains become larger, the cell walls break open and the potato becomes softer and easier to digest.

Paint

OCR B   C1   ✓
WJEC   C2   ✓

Paint is used to make surfaces look more attractive and to protect them from damage. The paint is put on to the surface in thin layers. The **solvent** in the paint **evaporates** and the paint dries. Paint is a special type of mixture called a **colloid**. Paints consist of a solvent to thin the paint out, a **pigment** to give the colour and a **binding medium** to make the pigment stick to the surface it is coating. In a colloid, the particles of the pigment mix throughout the paint but they are not dissolved in the solvent. Colloids do not separate because the particles are so small that they are fully dispersed throughout the mixture and do not settle to the bottom over time. Oil paints consist of pigment particles dispersed in oil and a solvent. The solvent evaporates and the oil is oxidised by oxygen in the air; this takes a long time so oil paints dry slowly.

Phosphorescent pigments take in energy and then release it later as light. They are used in a range of applications such as watch dials and decorations for young children's rooms.

Thermochromic pigments change colour as the temperature changes. They can be used to help monitor temperatures, for example, on bath toys, cups and cutlery for babies. Parents can see at a glance if the temperature is safe for their baby. They can also be used for fun applications such as mood rings. Thermochromic pigments may also be added to acrylic paints.

Washing-up liquid

OCR B   C6   ✓

Washing-up liquid is used in the kitchen to get plates and cutlery clean. Each ingredient has a specific function to help the cleaning process:

- **detergent**, to clean the object being washed
- water, to thin out the detergent so it is easy to dispense
- colouring and fragrance, to make it more appealing to users
- a rinse agent, to help the water run off the washed objects more easily.

PROGRESS CHECK

1. What is made during a chemical reaction?
2. Why are proteins needed by the body?
3. What is special about thermochromic pigments?
4. Why are paints used?
5. Explain how phosphorescent pigments work.
6. Explain why colloids do not separate over time.

6. Colloids do not separate because the particles are so small that they are fully dispersed throughout the mixture and do not settle to the bottom.
5. Phosphorescent pigments take in energy and then release it later as light.
4. To make surfaces more attractive and to protect them from damage.
3. They change colour as the temperature changes.
2. For growth and repair.
1. New substances.

2.9 The carbon cycle

LEARNING SUMMARY

After studying this section, you should be able to:

- Understand that carbon dioxide is a very small, but increasing, proportion of air.
- List processes that release carbon dioxide into the air.
- List processes that remove carbon dioxide from the air.
- Explain how human activities are upsetting the balance of the carbon cycle.
- Describe the properties of a good fuel.

Moving carbon around the carbon cycle

AQA	C1	✓
OCR A	C1	✓
OCR B	C1	✓
EDEXCEL	C1	✓
WJEC	C1	✓
CCEA	C2	✓

KEY POINT

The level of carbon dioxide in the atmosphere is fairly constant. This is because of the carbon cycle.

This cycle moves carbon between the atmosphere, the oceans and rocks.

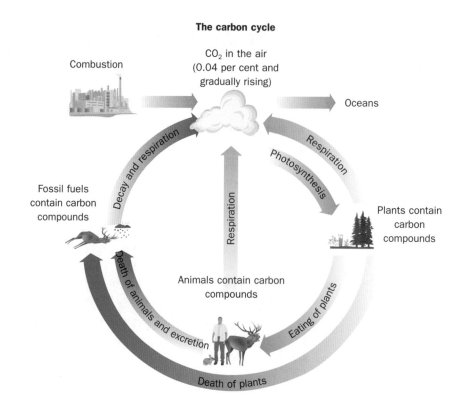

The carbon cycle

- Plants take in carbon from the atmosphere during photosynthesis.
- Plants and animals return carbon to the atmosphere during respiration.
- Fossil fuels release carbon into the atmosphere during combustion (burning).

Carbon is also recycled in the sea.

> Make a poster to show how carbon is moved between the atmosphere, oceans and rocks. Make sure you annotate each stage.

1. Marine organism shells are made of carbonates. The shells drop to the sea bed as the organisms die.
2. The shells fossilise to become limestone rock.
3. Volcanic eruptions heat the limestone and release carbon dioxide into the atmosphere. Carbon dioxide is also released during weathering of the limestone rock.
4. Oceans absorbing carbon dioxide act as **carbon sinks**.

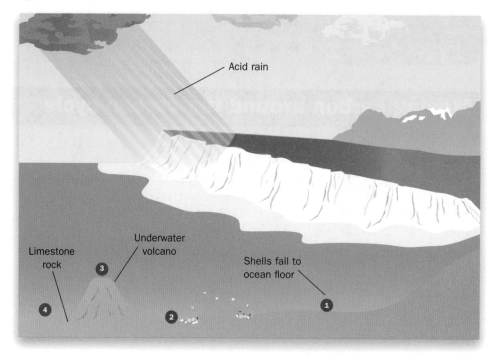

The carbon cycle and fossil fuels

AQA	C3	✓
OCR B	C1	✓
EDEXCEL	C1	✓
WJEC	C1	✓
CCEA	C2	✓

As the world's population expands, and with greater worldwide industrialisation, the overall levels of fossil fuels being burned is increasing. This means more carbon dioxide is being released into the atmosphere. As fossil fuels are thought to contribute towards the greenhouse effect, alternative fuels are being developed. A good fuel should be:

- easy to store and transport
- inexpensive to buy
- non-polluting
- easy to burn
- produce little ash or smoke
- non-toxic
- widely available
- efficient when it is burned (produce lots of energy).

PROGRESS CHECK

1. Name three places where large amounts of carbon are found.
2. Why is more carbon dioxide now being released into the atmosphere?
3. Name three fossil fuels.
4. How do plants take in carbon?
5. What is happening to the world's population?
6. Carbon moves between the atmosphere, the oceans and rocks through a series of steps called the carbon cycle. Explain why the levels of carbon dioxide in the atmosphere have remained almost constant.

1. In the atmosphere, oceans and in rocks.
2. More fossil fuels are being burned.
3. Coal, oil and gas.
4. By photosynthesis.
5. It is increasing.
6. There is a balance between plants taking in carbon from the atmosphere during photosynthesis, plants and animals returning carbon to the atmosphere during respiration and fossil fuels releasing carbon dioxide into the atmosphere during combustion (burning).

Sample GCSE questions

1 In 1912, Alfred Wegener proposed that the Earth's major continents had once been joined together, in a 'supercontinent', named 'Pangea'.

(a) **(i)** How did Wegener explain how the continents had moved into their current positions? **[3]**

The continents are separate plates, which float on the molten magma and move because of convection currents.

← Get as much information in as you can!

(ii) Why might other scientists have found Wegener's ideas hard to accept? **[2]**

The movement is too slow to have been measurable at the time. The majority would have believed that the Earth was as God had created it, because religious teaching was stronger than scientific teaching at the time.

(iii) Use the diagram to describe one piece of evidence that helped Wegener arrive at his theory. **[2]**

The shapes of the continents are such that they appear to 'fit together', like pieces of a giant jigsaw puzzle.

← When it says 'use the diagram', you cannot use other evidence than what the diagram shows.

(b) **(i)** Use Wegener's theory to explain why Britain has rocks that were originally formed in tropical swamps and others that can only have been formed in deserts. **[2]**

Britain is on a continental plate that has moved through different climate zones through the ages.

← Remember that the theory of moving plates has to be explicitly mentioned in this answer.

(ii) Explain how fossil records helped to support Wegener's theory. **[3]**

Fossils from different continents showed the same animal and plant species had been present in the same eras. This suggests the continents were once joined, as it would be an unlikely coincidence if the continents had been separated by the oceans, as they are today.

Sample GCSE questions

2 The majority of soft drinks sold in the UK are now sold in plastic bottles. Although most plastic bottles carry the recycling symbol, a large number end up in conventional rubbish bins, from which they are taken and dumped in landfill sites.

(a) Why is it a problem that plastic bottles are dumped in landfill sites? [2]

The bottles are non-biodegradable, so they will remain in the landfill for many years.

(b) As an alternative to dumping the bottles in landfill sites, the bottles could be:

● reused by being refilled with drinks
● recycled by melting the plastic and making new plastic products
● burned to provide heat energy in power stations.

Use your knowledge and understanding to compare the advantages and disadvantages of these three alternatives, in relation to their cost and their impact on the environment. [6]

The quality of written communication will be assessed in your answer to this question.

The advantage of reusing would be that no more bottles would have to be made, saving resources and energy.

Bottles would not be dumped in landfill unless damaged.

To reuse bottles they would have to be undamaged. They would have to be collected, cleaned and sterilised, which could cost a lot.

The advantage of recycling is that the plastic is not wasted or dumped in landfill.

To recycle the bottles, different plastics have to be sorted and separated. It takes energy to melt the plastic.

Burning provides energy which would otherwise come from fossil fuels, a non-renewable resource.

Burning plastics causes pollution as they do not burn with a clean flame.

Marks will be awarded depending on the number of relevant points included in the answer and the spelling, punctuation and grammar. In this question there are 9 relevant points, so 7 or 9 with good spelling, punctuation and grammar will gain full marks.

When you have written your answer, check that you have covered every aspect you were asked to write about. Read it back, silently to yourself, to ensure it makes sense.

Exam practice questions

1 Earth's early atmosphere contained a much higher proportion of carbon dioxide than it does, today.

(a) What name is given to the process by which green plants remove carbon dioxide from the atmosphere?

.... **[1]**

(b) Which gas is produced and released into the atmosphere by this process?

.... **[1]**

(c) How might deforestation increase the atmospheric carbon dioxide?

....

.... **[2]**

2 Air is a mixture of gases.

(a) What is the name of the technique which can be used to separate the gases?

.... **[1]**

(b) What property of the gases allows them to be separated in this way?

.... **[1]**

(c) Which two gases are the most abundant in air?

.... **[2]**

3 Clean air contains a mixture of gases. The proportions of these gases are shown in the pie chart below.

Nitrogen (78%)

Oxygen

Other gases (1%)

(a) Which gas makes up most of the air?

.... **[1]**

(b) What percentage of the air is made up of oxygen?

.... **[1]**

(c) Give an example of a gas that would be found in 'other gases'.

.... **[1]**

Exam practice questions

4 Many non-biodegradable plastics end up in landfill sites, where they will persist for many hundreds of years.

(a) What do you understand by the term 'non-biodegradable'?

.... **[1]**

(b) Plastics are flammable, but burning is not a good way to dispose of them. Why not?

.... **[1]**

(c) Give two examples of ways people can avoid disposing of plastics in landfill sites.

.... **[2]**

5 The ozone layer is made of O_3 molecules and stops UV light hitting the surface of the Earth.

Explain why CFCs are harmful to the ozone layer.

....

.... **[2]**

6 David and Lisa measure the concentration of sulfur dioxide gas in the air starting at the centre of town and moving out into the countryside. Their results are shown in the table.

Distance from town centre (km)	0	2	4	6	8	10
Sulfur dioxide level ($\mu g/m^3$)	122	113	95	83	116	82

David claims the results show that the greater distance you are from the town centre the less air pollution there is. Comment on David's claim and discuss how they could improve their evidence.

....

....

.... **[3]**

7 Explain how cutting down large areas of rainforest in South America affects the Earth's atmosphere.

....

....

....

....

.... **[5]**

8 Helium is a noble gas. It is very unreactive and it does not form compounds with other elements.

(a) Why is helium preferred to hydrogen for use in modern airships?

.... **[2]**

(b) Argon can be extracted from air. Why can it not be used in airships?

.... **[1]**

Exam practice questions

9 Cooking of food can improve its texture and flavour. It kills bacteria and it may also make the food easier to digest.

(a) Why is cooking food an example of a chemical reaction?

.... [1]

(b) What happens to protein molecules when food is cooked?

.... [1]

(c) Explain why cooking potato makes it easier to digest.

.... [2]

10 Catalytic converters are fitted to most modern cars, to reduce pollution from exhaust gases.

(a) Complete the balanced equation showing how the catalytic converter works.

$2CO(g) + 2NO(g) \rightarrow$ .... + ... [2]

(b) Why is it important to remove oxides of nitrogen from exhaust gases?

.... [1]

(c) Why does a car with a catalytic converter still pollute the atmosphere?

.... [1]

11 Describe what happens when a continental plate and an oceanic plate collide.

....

....

.... [3]

12 The early atmosphere of the Earth was much more like the atmosphere of our neighbouring planets, Mars and Venus.

Explain how changes in the Earth's atmosphere have led to it being a much cooler planet than either of its nearest neighbours, and able to support life.

The quality of written communication will be assessed in your answer to this question.

....

....

....

....

....

....

....

.... [6]

3 Organic chemistry and analysis

The following topics are covered in this chapter:

- Organic chemistry 1
- Fuels
- Vegetable oils
- Plastics
- Ethanol
- Organic chemistry 2
- Analysis
- Cosmetics

3.1 Organic chemistry 1

LEARNING SUMMARY

After studying this section, you should be able to:

- Understand that 'organic' chemicals are compounds of carbon covalently bonded to other elements.
- Recognise an alkane from its general formula.
- Understand the terms 'homologous series' and 'isomerism'
- Recognise the differences between the formulae of alkanes and alkenes.
- Describe how bromine water can be used to test for an alkene.

The importance of carbon

AQA	C1	✓
OCR B	C1	✓
EDEXCEL	C3	✓
WJEC	C2, C3	✓
CCEA	C2	✓

KEY POINT

Carbon atoms have the ability to form four bonds with other atoms. This means that carbon atoms can be made into a large range of compounds. These compounds are the basis of life and the chemistry of these compounds is called **organic** chemistry.

Organic compounds contain **covalent bonds**.

Covalent bonding involves the sharing of electrons. The shared pairs of electrons hold the atoms together.

Alkanes

AQA	C1	✓
OCR A	C7	✓
OCR B	C1	✓
EDEXCEL	C1, C3	✓
WJEC	C2, C3	✓
CCEA	C2	✓

The **alkanes** are a family of **hydrocarbon** molecules. Most of the compounds in crude oil are hydrocarbons. This means that alkanes only contain hydrogen and carbon atoms. Scientists describe alkanes as **saturated** hydrocarbons. This is because they contain no carbon double bonds (C=C bonds) and so already contain the maximum number of hydrogen atoms. The alkanes are an example of an **homologous series**: all alkanes have the same general formula and similar chemical properties. Their physical properties, for example, boiling points, gradually vary down the series.

Name	Methane	Ethane	Propane	Butane
Chemical Formula	CH_4	C_2H_6	C_3H_8	C_4H_{10}
Structure	H | H–C–H | H	H H | | H–C–C–H | | H H	H H H | | | H–C–C–C–H | | | H H H	H H H H | | | | H–C–C–C–C–H | | | | H H H H

> Practise drawing out the different alkane molecules shown in the table.

Alkanes are useful fuels: complete combustion of alkanes produces carbon dioxide and water.

Alkanes have the general formula C_nH_{2n+2}. **Ball and stick models** are a useful way of showing the three-dimensional position of atoms and bonds. The ball and stick model of methane, CH_4, is shown below.

Ball and stick model of methane

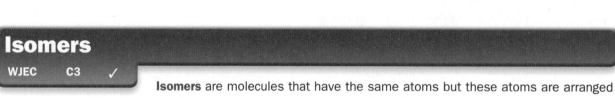

> If you are given a molecular formula that obeys the rules for the general formula of an alkane, then you can tell it is an alkane molecule without having to draw it out.

Isomers

Isomers are molecules that have the same atoms but these atoms are arranged in different ways. Isomers have the same molecular formula but a different structural formula and displayed formula.

The carbon chain for some alkanes can be either branched or unbranched and this can cause **isomerism**.

The isomers of C_4H_{10} are shown below.

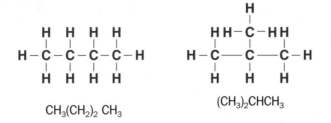

$CH_3(CH_2)_2 CH_3$

$(CH_3)_2CHCH_3$

The isomers of C_5H_{12} are shown below.

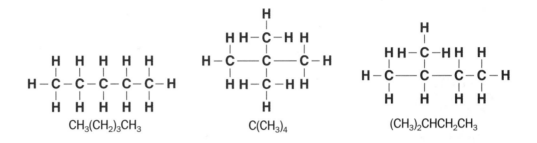

$CH_3(CH_2)_3CH_3$

$C(CH_3)_4$

$(CH_3)_2CHCH_2CH_3$

Alkenes

AQA	C1	✓
OCR B	C1	✓
EDEXCEL	C1, C3	✓
WJEC	C2, C3	✓
CCEA	C2	✓

The **alkenes** are also hydrocarbon molecules. Scientists describe alkenes as **unsaturated** hydrocarbons because they all contain one or more C=C bond. They are produced by cracking longer chain alkane molecules. The single lines in the diagrams represent a single covalent bond while the double lines represent a double covalent bond.

Name	Ethene	Propene
Chemical Formula	C_2H_4	C_3H_6
Structure	$H_2C=CH_2$	$H_2C=CH-CH_3$

Reactions of alkenes

AQA	C1	✓
OCR B	C1	✓
EDEXCEL	C1	✓
WJEC	C2, C3	✓
CCEA	C2	✓

Alkenes are more reactive than alkanes owing to the presence of C=C bonds. This means alkenes are more useful because they can be used to make new substances. Alkenes have the general formula C_nH_{2n}. Butene has the formula C_4H_8.

Reaction of alkenes with bromine

OCR B	C1	✓
EDEXCEL	C1	✓
WJEC	C2	✓
CCEA	C2	✓

KEY POINT

Alkenes also react with bromine water. Bromine water is **decolourised** in the presence of alkenes.

When alkenes react with bromine water an addition reaction occurs (the two molecules add together to form one molecule).

> Learn the product made when alkenes react with bromine.

The bromine from the bromine water adds to the alkene: one bromine atom is added to each of the carbon atoms involved in the double bond. This forms a colourless dibromo compound. In the diagram below, ethene is reacting with bromine to form a dibromo compound.

> When describing the test for unsaturation, make sure you describe the resulting solution as colourless, not clear.

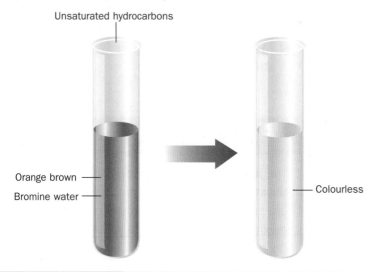

Unsaturated hydrocarbons

Orange brown — Bromine water

— Colourless

KEY POINT

Alkanes do not contain C=C bonds so they do not react with bromine water.

PROGRESS CHECK

1. How many bonds can carbon atoms form?
2. Why are alkanes described as saturated hydrocarbons?
3. What is the name of the first member of the alkane family?
4. Which family does ethene belong to?
5. What is the formula of butane?
6. Consider these compounds:

   $C_{56}H_{112}$ C_2H_5OH $C_{18}H_{38}$

   a) Which of these compounds belongs to the alkene family?
   b) Which of these compounds belongs to the alkane family?

6. a) $C_{56}H_{112}$ b) $C_{18}H_{38}$
5. C_4H_{10}
4. Alkenes.
3. Methane.
2. 'Saturated' means they contain no double bonds; 'hydrocarbons' contain hydrogen and carbon atoms only.
1. Four.

3.2 Fuels

LEARNING SUMMARY		

After studying this section, you should be able to:

- Explain how fossil fuels were formed.
- Recall that crude oil is a mixture of hydrocarbons.
- Explain how fractional distillation is used to separate crude oil.
- Describe how differences in chain length determine the properties of hydrocarbons.
- Understand how and why cracking of hydrocarbons is carried out.

Formation of fossil fuels

OCR A	C1	✓
OCR B	C1	✓
EDEXCEL	C1	✓
WJEC	C1	✓

Coal is mainly carbon. Petrol, diesel and oil are hydrocarbons.

Fuels are burned to release energy. In the UK, the **fossil fuels** coal, oil and natural gas are widely used. The burning of fuels is an **exothermic** reaction. The products of crude oil can also be used to make a wide range of useful materials. Fossil fuels are formed over millions of years from the fossilised remains of dead plants and animals. When the plants and animals died, they fell to the sea or swamp floor. Occasionally, the remains were covered by **sediment** very quickly. In the absence of oxygen, the remains did not decay. Over time, more layers of sediment gradually built up. The lower layers became heated and **pressurised**. Over millions of years, fossil fuels formed. Fossil fuels are **non-renewable** so crude oil is a **finite** resource. These take millions of years to form, but are being used up very quickly.

Crude oil

AQA	C1	✓
OCR A	C2	✓
OCR B	C1	✓
EDEXCEL	C1	✓
WJEC	C1	✓
CCEA	C2	✓

Crude oil is a mixture of many substances but the most important are **hydrocarbons**. Hydrocarbons are molecules that only contain carbon and hydrogen atoms. Some of the hydrocarbons have very short chains of carbon atoms. These hydrocarbons:

- are not very **viscous** (i.e. runny)
- are easy to **ignite**
- have low boiling points
- are valuable fuels.

Other hydrocarbon molecules have much longer chains of carbon atoms. These hydrocarbon molecules:

- are more viscous (less runny) than shorter chain ones
- are harder to ignite
- have higher boiling points.

These longer hydrocarbon molecules are less useful as fuels than shorter chain ones. However, before any of these hydrocarbon molecules can be used, they must first be separated into groups of molecules with a similar number of carbon atoms, called fractions.

In compounds, the atoms of two or more different elements are chemically combined. In mixtures, two or more different elements or compounds are simply mixed together. Each constituent part of the mixture has its original chemical properties. This makes it quite easy to separate mixtures.

Fractional distillation of crude oil

AQA	C1	✓
OCR A	C2	✓
OCR B	C1	✓
EDEXCEL	C1	✓
WJEC	C1, C2	✓
CCEA	C2	✓

The components of crude oil can be separated by fractional distillation. First, the crude oil is heated until it **evaporates** and enters the fractionating column. The diagram of the fractionating column shows that the bottom of the column is much hotter than the top of the column.

> **KEY POINT**
>
> This means that short hydrocarbon molecules can reach the top of the column before they **condense** and are collected. Longer hydrocarbon molecules condense at higher temperatures and are collected at different points down the column.

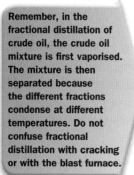

Remember, in the fractional distillation of crude oil, the crude oil mixture is first vaporised. The mixture is then separated because the different fractions condense at different temperatures. Do not confuse fractional distillation with cracking or with the blast furnace.

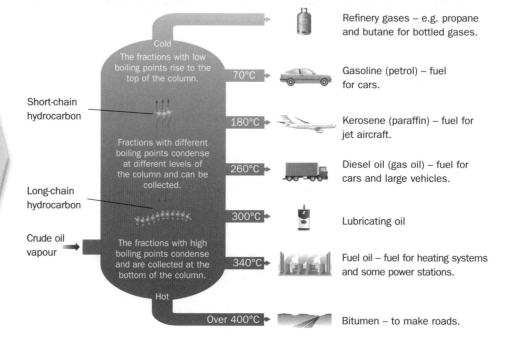

Refinery gases – e.g. propane and butane for bottled gases.

Gasoline (petrol) – fuel for cars. 70°C

Kerosene (paraffin) – fuel for jet aircraft. 180°C

Diesel oil (gas oil) – fuel for cars and large vehicles. 260°C

Lubricating oil 300°C

Fuel oil – fuel for heating systems and some power stations. 340°C

Bitumen – to make roads. Over 400°C

The forces of attraction between the hydrocarbon molecules are much weaker than the forces of attraction within the molecules. The larger the hydrocarbon molecule is, the stronger the forces of attraction between the molecules are, so more energy is required to overcome the force of attraction. Larger hydrocarbon molecules have higher boiling points.

Using different fractions of crude oil

OCR A	C2	✓
OCR B	C1	✓
EDEXCEL	C1	✓
WJEC	C1	✓
CCEA	C2	✓

The different fractions obtained from crude oil have different uses.

- Liquid petroleum gas (LPG) contains propane and butane. These gases are used in domestic heating and cooking.
- Petrol is used as a fuel for some cars.
- Kerosene is used as a fuel for aeroplanes.
- Diesel oil is used as a fuel for some cars, lorries and trains.
- Fuel oil is used as a fuel for large ships and power stations.
- Bitumen is used to make roads and roofs.

Cracking

AQA	C1	✓
OCR B	C1	✓
EDEXCEL	C1	✓
WJEC	C1	✓
CCEA	C2	✓

The large hydrocarbon molecules separated during the fractional distillation of crude oil are not very useful.

> **KEY POINT**
>
> However, these hydrocarbon molecules can be broken down into smaller, more useful and more valuable molecules by a process called **cracking**.

The cracking of long chain hydrocarbons is carried out on a large scale. First, the long hydrocarbon molecules are heated until they evaporate. The vapour is then passed over a hot aluminium oxide catalyst. In this example, decane is being cracked to produce octane and ethene.

decane $C_{10}H_{22}$ $\longrightarrow$ octane C_8H_{18} + ethene C_2H_4
(from the naphtha fraction)

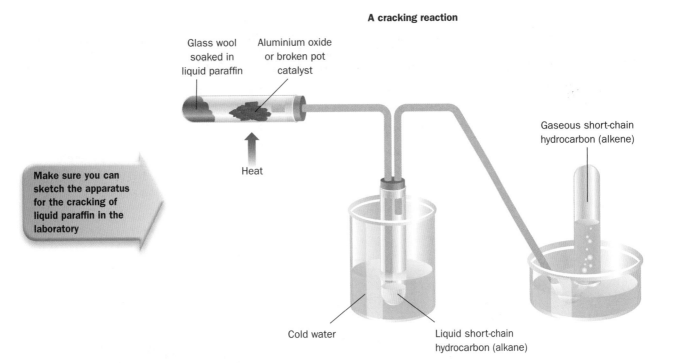

Make sure that when you balance equations for cracking you have the same number of each type of atom on both sides of the equation.

Octane is one of the hydrocarbon molecules in petrol. Ethene, a member of the alkene family of hydrocarbons, is also produced. Ethene is used to make a range of new compounds including plastics and industrial alcohol. As we only have a finite amount of crude oil left, scientists are working to find replacement fuels for the future.

A cracking reaction

Glass wool soaked in liquid paraffin

Aluminium oxide or broken pot catalyst

Heat

Gaseous short-chain hydrocarbon (alkene)

Cold water

Liquid short-chain hydrocarbon (alkane)

> Make sure you can sketch the apparatus for the cracking of liquid paraffin in the laboratory

Cracking is an example of a thermal decomposition reaction. Some of the products of cracking, for example, petrol and diesel, are very useful fuels.

PROGRESS CHECK

1. How long does it take for fossil fuels to form?
2. Which elements are found in hydrocarbon molecules?
3. Give three properties of short chain hydrocarbon molecules.
4. Which hydrocarbons make the best fuels?
5. What does a 'fraction' mean in this context?
6. Describe why larger hydrocarbon molecules have higher boiling points than smaller hydrocarbons.

1. It takes millions of years.
2. Hydrogen and carbon.
3. Three from: runny; easy to ignite; have low boiling points; are valuable fuels.
4. Short chain hydrocarbons.
5. A group of compounds with a similar number of carbon atoms.
6. The larger the hydrocarbon molecule is, the stronger the forces of attraction between the molecules are, so more energy is required to overcome the force of attraction.

3.3 Vegetable oils

LEARNING SUMMARY

After studying this section, you should be able to:

- Recognise that vegetable oils are extracted from the seeds of a variety of plants.
- Recall that vegetable oils can be processed to make biofuels and soap.
- Understand the difference between saturated and unsaturated fats.
- Describe what an 'emulsion' is.
- Explain why vegetable oils may be hydrogenated to make margarine.

Using vegetable oils

| AQA | C1 | ✓ |
| OCR B | C6 | ✓ |

Vegetable oils are often removed by crushing up the plant material and collecting the oil. Other oils are collected using distillation. These processes remove water and other impurities to produce pure oil.

Fats have higher boiling points than water. Cooking food by frying is therefore much faster than cooking food in boiling water. In addition, frying foods produces interesting new flavours and increases the energy content of the food.

Fuels and soaps

AQA	C1	✓
OCR A	C7	✓
OCR B	C6	✓
EDEXCEL	C3	✓

To get a top grade, you need to know the word equation that sums up this reaction.

fat + sodium hydroxide → soap + glycerol

This is a hydrolysis reaction.

When vegetable oils are burned they release lots of energy. In fact, vegetable oils can be used in place of fossil fuels in the form of **biodiesel**. This is an alternative to diesel produced from crude oil. Fuels made from plant materials are called **biofuels**.

Oils and fats are **esters**. Soap can be produced by reacting vegetable oils or animal fats with hot sodium or potassium hydroxide solution. The process is known as **saponification** and also produces glycerol. Soaps are the sodium or potassium salts of carboxylic acids with long carbon chains.

Emulsions

| AQA | C1 | ✓ |
| OCR B | C1, C6 | ✓ |

Oils do not dissolve in water. Salad dressing is an example of a type of everyday mixture called an **emulsion**. It is a mixture of two liquids: oil and water containing the vinegar. Salad dressing is made by shaking oil and vinegar so that they mix together. After a short while, however, the oil and vinegar separate out to form two distinct layers. If the salad dressing was placed in a separating funnel, the lower, denser layer could be run off leaving the less dense layer in the separating funnel. An emulsion is thicker than either of its separate parts. Emulsions have some special properties that make them very useful. Emulsions can improve a product's texture, appearance or ability to coat foodstuffs. Emulsions are widely used to make:

- ice creams
- mayonnaise
- cosmetics
- paints.

Milk is an oil-in-water emulsion. Butter is a water-in-fat emulsion.

Emulsifiers

| AQA | C1 | ✓ |
| OCR B | C1, C6 | ✓ |

Emulsifiers are molecules with two very different ends. In a salad dressing, one end of the emulsifier molecule is attracted to the oil, while the other end is attracted to the water in the vinegar. The addition of emulsifier molecules keeps the two liquids mixed together.

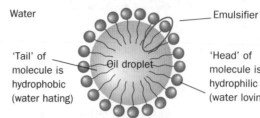

Simple model of an emulsifier

Water

Emulsifier

'Tail' of molecule is hydrophobic (water hating)

Oil droplet

'Head' of molecule is hydrophilic (water loving)

Saturated and unsaturated fats

OCR A	C7	✓
OCR B	C6	✓
EDEXCEL	C1	✓

Animal fats are usually solid, or nearly solid, at room temperature. A **saturated** fat contains many C–C bonds but no C=C bonds. Scientists believe that people who eat lots of saturated fats may develop raised blood cholesterol levels. This is linked with an increased risk of heart disease. Most vegetable fats are liquids at room temperature and so are described as oils.

Identifying vegetable oils

AQA	C1	✓
OCR A	C7	✓
OCR B	C6	✓

Vegetable oils contain C=C bonds. Scientists describe these molecules as **unsaturated** fats because they could hold more hydrogen atoms. The presence of the C=C bonds affects the way that the fatty acids in the molecule can pack together. C=C bonds are rigid and their presence causes kinks so that the fatty acids cannot pack closely together. Unsaturated fats have lower melting points than saturated fats. While most vegetable fats are liquid at room temperature, most animal fats are solids. Bromine water can be used to detect the presence of the C=C bonds in vegetable oils. If the double bonds are present the bromine water decolourises and a colourless dibromo compound is formed.

Hydrogenated vegetable oils

AQA	C1	✓
OCR B	C6	✓

KEY POINT

Vegetable oils are often liquids at room temperature because they contain C=C bonds. There are, however, advantages to using fats that are solid at room temperature.

They are easier to spread and can be used to make new products such as cakes and pastries.

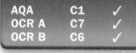

Hydrogenation produces more saturated fat, which is harmful to health.

Vegetable oils can be made solid at room temperature by a process known as **hydrogenation**. The oils are heated to 60°C with hydrogen and a nickel catalyst. The hydrogen atoms add across double bonds to form fats that are solid at room temperature. Hydrogenated vegetable oils also have a longer shelf life.

Food additives

OCR B	C1	✓

Scientists often add chemicals to improve foods. The chemicals that have passed safety tests and are approved for use throughout the European Union are assigned **E-numbers** to help identify and categorise them. Chemicals that are commonly added to foods include:

Make sure you are able to say why each of these common additives are put in foodstuffs.

- **colours**, which are added to make food look more attractive
- **flavours**, which are added to enhance taste
- **antioxidants**, which stop foods from reacting with oxygen.

PROGRESS CHECK

1. Which parts of plants can we obtain oils from?
2. What are biofuels?
3. Which vitamins do we obtain from eating fats?
4. Why are antioxidants added to foods?
5. A new fat is found that is liquid at room temperature.
   a) Is this fat likely to be saturated or unsaturated?
   b) Is this fat likely to have come from a plant or an animal?
   c) How could you test if this fat was saturated or unsaturated?

c) Add bromine water – if the fat decolourises the bromine water it is unsaturated.
b) Plant.
5. a) Unsaturated.
4. To stop them reacting with oxygen.
3. Vitamins A and D.
2. Fuels made from plant materials.
1. Fruits, seeds and nuts.

3.4 Plastics

After studying this section, you should be able to:

- Understand the term polymer and recall some examples of polymers.
- Describe what happens in an addition polymerisation reaction.
- Write equations to represent polymerisation reactions.
- Explain the difference between thermoplastic and thermosetting materials.
- Relate the properties of plastics to their uses.

LEARNING SUMMARY

Polymerisation

AQA	C1	✓
OCR A	C2	✓
OCR B	C1	✓
EDEXCEL	C1, C3	✓
WJEC	C1, C2	✓
CCEA	C2	✓

Plastics are **synthetic** (manufactured) **polymers**. **Natural polymers** include cotton, wood, leather, silk and wool. In polymers, lots of small molecules are joined together to make one big molecule.

The simplest **alkene**, ethene, can be formed by the cracking of large **hydrocarbon** molecules. If ethene is heated under pressure in the presence of a **catalyst**, many ethene molecules can join together to form a larger molecule called poly(ethene) or polythene. The diagram below shows how a large number of ethene molecules join together to form polythene.

The 'n' at the start of the equation and the section of the polymer surrounded by brackets represents the number of molecules involved. The brackets are used because it would be impractical to write out the complete structure. The brackets surround a representative unit that is then repeated through the whole polymer. The small starting molecules, in this case the ethene molecules, are called **monomers**. The C=C bonds in the ethene molecules join together to form long chain molecules called **polymers**. So, a polymer is made from lots of monomer units; in fact, 'poly' means lots. This is an example of an **addition polymerisation** reaction. The ethene molecules have simply joined together.

Other polymers

AQA	C2	✓
OCR A	C2	✓
OCR B	C1	✓
EDEXCEL	C1, C3	✓
WJEC	C1, C2	✓
CCEA	C2	✓

Polymerisation reactions may involve other monomer units. The exact properties of the polymer formed depend upon:

- the monomers involved
- the conditions under which it was made
- the length of the polymer chains.

For example, low density polythene and high density polythene have very different properties and uses because they are produced using different catalysts and different conditions. A plastic's properties are also affected by the amount of **crystallinity** of its structure. The more crystalline a plastic is the more brittle it will be.

Addition polymerisation reactions

AQA	C1	✓
OCR A	C2	✓
OCR B	C1	✓
EDEXCEL	C1	✓
WJEC	C1, C2	✓
CCEA	C2	✓

Polymer	Description	Image
Polypropene	Made by an addition polymerisation reaction between many propene molecules.	
Polyvinyl chloride (PVC)	Made by an addition polymerisation reaction between many chloroethene molecules. Chloroethene used to be called vinyl chloride.	
Polytetra-fluoroethene (PTFE or Teflon)	Made by an addition polymerisation reaction between many tetrafluoroethene molecules.	PTFE is known as 'Teflon'. Surfaces coated in Teflon have low friction. It is used to coat some frying pans and saucepans.

Thermoplastics and thermosetting plastics

AQA	C2	✓
OCR A	C2	✓
OCR B	C1	✓
WJEC	C2	✓

Thermoplastics consist of long polymer chains with a few cross-links.

Long chains of molecules

Weak intermolecular forces between chains.

When heated, the material softens. It can then be reshaped. On cooling, the material becomes solid and stiff again because cross-links are made. Thermoplastics can be heated and reshaped many times. Polythene is a thermoplastic. Thermoplastics can be stretched easily.

Thermosetting plastics consist of long, heavily cross-linked polymer chains.

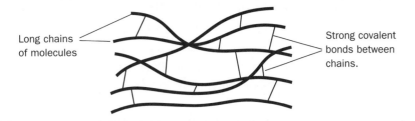

Long chains of molecules

Strong covalent bonds between chains.

When they are first made these thermosetting plastics are soft and can be shaped. Once they have set, however, they become solid and stiff. They do not soften again, even if they are heated to very high temperatures, and so they cannot be reshaped. Melamine is a thermosetting plastic. Thermosetting plastics are rigid and cannot be stretched.

New polymers

AQA	C1	✓
OCR A	C2	✓
WJEC	C1	✓

Scientists are developing new and exciting polymers that have a wide range of uses, for example:

- dental polymers
- wound dressings
- hydrogels
- shape memory alloys (SMA).

Uses of plastics

AQA	C1	✓
OCR A	C2	✓
OCR B	C1	✓
EDEXCEL	C1	✓
WJEC	C1	✓

Polymers have some very useful properties. They are:

- flexible
- good thermal and electrical insulators
- resistant to corrosion
- waterproof
- easy to mould and shape as they generally have low melting points.

The table shows some different plastics and their properties.

Plastic	Description
Polythene	Polythene is cheap and strong. It is used to make plastic bags and bottles. Polythene bags are cheaper than the paper bags they have widely replaced.
PVC	PVC is rigid and can be used for building materials such as drainpipes. PVC has replaced metal drainpipes because PVC is cheaper and lighter than metal. Chemicals called **plasticisers** can be added to PVC to make products such as Wellington boots and mackintoshes.
Polypropene	Polypropene is strong and has a high elasticity. It is used for crates and ropes.
Polystyrene	Polystyrene is cheap and can be moulded into different shapes. It is used for packaging and for plastic casings.

Nylon and polyester

OCR B   C1   ✓

Nylon and polyester are condensation polymers that are used to make clothes. Nylon can be used to make cheap waterproof jackets. Nylon is lightweight, hard wearing, keeps UV light out and is waterproof, but it is not breathable so perspiration can make a nylon jacket quite uncomfortable to wear.

Gore-tex™

OCR B   C1   ✓

More expensive Gore-tex™ jackets are breathable. Gore-tex™ consists of a thin membrane of PTFE, which is used to coat nylon fabrics. The membrane has lots of little holes. Liquid water is too big to go through these holes, so the fabric is waterproof. Water vapour is small enough to pass through the holes, so it is breathable.

PROGRESS CHECK

1. What type of reaction is involved in the formation of polythene?
2. What is the name given to the small units that join together to form a polymer?
3. Teflon is used to coat frying pans. This coating helps to prevent food from sticking to the pan during cooking. Teflon is made from the monomer tetrafluoroethene.
   a) Draw a tetrafluoroethene molecule.
   b) Is a tetrafluoroethene molecule saturated or unsaturated? Explain your answer.
   c) Draw the repeating unit for the polymer made from the addition polymerisation of tetrafluoroethene molecules.

PROGRESS CHECK

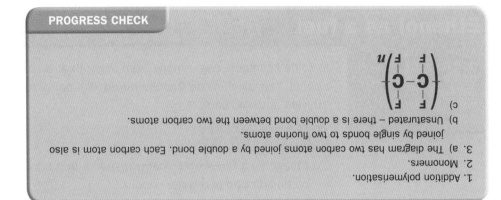

c)

b) Unsaturated – there is a double bond between the two carbon atoms.

joined by single bonds to two fluorine atoms.

3. a) The diagram has two carbon atoms joined by a double bond. Each carbon atom is also

2. Monomers.

1. Addition polymerisation.

3.5 Ethanol

LEARNING SUMMARY

After studying this section, you should be able to:

- Recall some important uses of ethanol.
- Describe how ethanol may be produced by fermentation of glucose.
- Describe how ethanol may be produced by hydration of ethene.
- Compare the advantages and disadvantages of both methods of production.
- Recall some properties of ethanoic acid.

Ethanol

AQA	C1, C3	✓
OCR A	C7	✓
OCR B	C6	✓
EDEXCEL	C3	✓
WJEC	C3	✓
CCEA	C2	✓

Ethanol, C_2H_5OH, is a member of the **alcohol** family of organic compounds. The diagram below shows the structure of ethanol. It is not a hydrocarbon because it contains an oxygen atom as well as carbon and hydrogen atoms.

$$H-\overset{\overset{\displaystyle H}{|}}{\underset{\underset{\displaystyle H}{|}}{C}}-\overset{\overset{\displaystyle H}{|}}{\underset{\underset{\displaystyle H}{|}}{C}}-O-H$$

Uses of ethanol

AQA	C1, C3	✓
OCR A	C7	✓
OCR B	C6	✓
EDEXCEL	C3	✓
WJEC	C1, C3	✓
CCEA	C2	✓

Ethanol is found in drinks like beer and wine. It is, however, toxic in large amounts. Ethanol has many useful properties. It is a good **solvent** and **evaporates** quickly. Many aftershaves contain ethanol. Ethanol is an important raw material and can also be used as a fuel.

Methanol is another member of the alcohol group and is even more toxic than ethanol. If someone was to drink methanol, they could become blind or even die. Methylated spirit is a mixture of ethanol, methanol and a purple dye. The purple dye is there to warn people about its toxicity; its unpleasant taste is to prevent people from drinking it. Methanol is a good solvent.

Ethanol as a fuel

AQA	C1, C3	✓
OCR A	C7	✓
OCR B	C6	✓
EDEXCEL	C1, C3	✓
WJEC	C3	✓
CCEA	C2	✓

In some countries, sugar made from sugar beet or sugar cane is made into alcohol. This alcohol can then be mixed with petrol to produce a fuel for vehicles, such as cars.

> **KEY POINT**
>
> Ethanol is a **renewable** energy resource that burns very cleanly, producing carbon dioxide and water vapour.

Alcohols, however, release less energy than petrol when they are burned. In order to produce enough alcohol for fuel, large areas of fertile land and a favourable climate are required to grow the plants needed. Producing fuels in this way is particularly attractive for countries that do not have large reserves of fossil fuels. However, if land is being used to grow crops to produce ethanol, this will reduce the amount of land available to grow food for people to eat.

The plants take in carbon from carbon dioxide during **photosynthesis** and then release the carbon as carbon dioxide when they are burned as fuels.

The fire triangle

WJEC	C3	✓

The **fire triangle** shows the three things that must be present to produce a fire:

- oxygen
- heat
- fuel.

If any one of these things is taken away, the fire will go out.

Fermentation

AQA	C1	✓
OCR A	C7	✓
OCR B	C6	✓
EDEXCEL	C3	✓
WJEC	C3	✓
CCEA	C2	✓

Fermentation has been used to make alcohol and alcoholic drinks for thousands of years. Fruits, vegetables and cereals are all sources of the sugar glucose, $C_6H_{12}O_6$. During fermentation, yeast is used to **catalyse** (speed up) the reaction in which glucose is converted into ethanol and carbon dioxide.

Make sure you can give the symbol equation for fermentation.

$C_6H_{12}O_6 \rightarrow 2C_2H_5OH + 2CO_2$

$$\text{glucose} \xrightarrow{\text{yeast}} \text{ethanol} + \text{carbon dioxide}$$

Conditions for fermentation

AQA	C1	✓
OCR A	C7	✓
OCR B	C6	✓
EDEXCEL	C3	✓
WJEC	C3	✓
CCEA	C2	✓

The temperature of the reaction has to be carefully controlled. If the temperature falls too low, the yeast becomes inactive and the rate of the reaction slows down. If the temperature rises too high, the yeast is denatured and stops working altogether. Temperatures between 25°C and 50°C work best. Water also needs to be present. Yeast is a fungus. It speeds up the **conversion** of sugar to alcohol and carbon dioxide, but is not itself used up in the process. Ethanol can also be made from waste biomass by genetically modified E. coli bacteria. The optimum conditions are:

- a pH of 6.0 to 7.0
- anaerobic conditions
- a warm temperature of around 30°C.

Fermentation

The fermentation lock allows carbon dioxide to escape, but stops oxygen in the air from reacting with the alcohol. This is important as ethanol can easily be oxidised by microbes to form ethanoic acid, which would make the drink taste sour.

Ethanol produced by fermentation has a concentration of around 6–14%. Some people prefer drinks with a higher alcohol content, such as whisky and brandy. These higher concentrations of alcohol are achieved by the process of fractional distillation. There is a very strong link, however, between the consumption of alcohol and an increased risk of accidents and raised levels of crime. Some religions prohibit the consumption of all alcoholic drinks.

Industrial alcohol

OCR A	C7	✓
OCR B	C6	✓
EDEXCEL	C3	✓
CCEA	C2	✓

There is another, more modern, way of producing vast amounts of very pure alcohol. Ethene (which is produced during the cracking of long chain hydrocarbons) is reacted with steam to produce ethanol.

ethene + steam → ethanol

The symbol equation to sum up the production of industrial alcohol is:

$$C_2H_4 + H_2O \rightarrow C_2H_5OH$$

A catalyst of **phosphoric acid** and a temperature of 300°C are used.

This method of producing ethanol is much cheaper than fermentation. It is a continuous, rather than a batch, process and because the reaction between ethene and steam is an **addition** reaction it has a higher atom economy than fermentation. Our reserves of fossil fuels are, however, finite and will run out one day.

PROGRESS CHECK

1. What is the formula of ethanol?
2. Why is ethanol not a hydrocarbon?
3. Which crops can be used to produce sugar for making alcohol?
4. What is the catalyst used in fermentation?
5. During fermentation reactions the temperature must be carefully controlled. What happens if the temperature falls too low or rises too high?

1. C_2H_5OH.
2. It contains oxygen as well as hydrogen and carbon.
3. Sugar beet and sugar cane.
4. Yeast.
5. If the temperature falls too low, the yeast becomes inactive and the rate of the reaction slows down. If the temperature rises too high, the yeast is denatured and stops working altogether.

3.6 Organic chemistry 2

LEARNING SUMMARY

After studying this section, you should be able to:

- Recognise members of the alcohol family by the presence of the hydroxyl group.
- Understand the term 'positional isomer'.
- Recognise members of the carboxylic acid family by the presence of the carboxyl group.
- Write equations to represent the formation of esters.
- Explain why carboxylic acids are weak acids.

Alcohols

AQA	C3	✓
OCR A	C7	✓
OCR B	C6	✓
EDEXCEL	C3	✓
WJEC	C3	✓
CCEA	C2	✓

The term **alcohol** is often used for the compound **ethanol**. In fact, ethanol is just one member of a family of organic compounds called alcohols. Alcohols contain the **hydroxyl**, OH, functional group and have the general formula $C_nH_{2n+1}OH$. Each member of the family differs from the previous one by the addition of a CH_2 group. Alcohols are **neutral** and react with carboxylic acids to form **esters**.

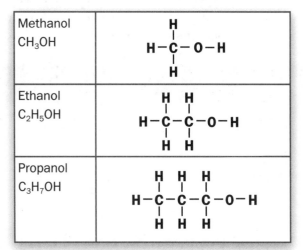

Methanol CH_3OH	
Ethanol C_2H_5OH	
Propanol C_3H_7OH	

Uses of alcohols

AQA	C3	✓
OCR A	C7	✓
OCR B	C6	✓
EDEXCEL	C3	✓
WJEC	C3	✓

Alcohols have a wide range of uses:

- They are good **solvents** for many compounds.
- They can be burned and used as **fuels**. The alcohol can either replace petrol or be mixed with petrol to improve **combustion**.
- Ethanol is the main alcohol found in alcoholic drinks such as beer.

Properties and reactions of alcohols

AQA	C3	✓
OCR A	C7	✓
EDEXCEL	C3	✓
WJEC	C3	✓

Methanol, ethanol and propanol all dissolve in water to form **neutral** solutions. The larger the alcohol molecule the less soluble in water it becomes. Alcohols react with sodium metal to form hydrogen gas and alkoxides.

sodium + ethanol → hydrogen + sodium ethoxide

The larger the alcohol molecule the more slowly it reacts with sodium.

Water also reacts with sodium to form sodium hydroxide and hydrogen.

Alkanes are saturated hydrocarbons and do not react with sodium.

The boiling points of alcohols are much higher than the boiling points of alkanes, which have the same number of carbon atoms, because there are stronger forces of attraction between the alcohol molecules than there are between the alkane molecules.

Alcohols can be burned in air. Complete combustion of ethanol produces carbon dioxide and water vapour. The alcohol is completely oxidised in this reaction.

ethanol + oxygen → carbon dioxide + water vapour

$$C_2H_5OH + 3O_2 \rightarrow 2CO_2 + 3H_2O$$

Ethanol can also be **oxidised** more gently by microbes or by chemical oxidising agents such as acidified potassium dichromate(VI). Primary alcohols can be oxidised to carboxylic acids.

Ethanol is oxidised to ethanoic acid. Over time, the ethanol in an opened bottle of an alcoholic drink will react with the oxygen in air to form ethanoic acid, leaving the drink with a distinctive vinegary smell and taste. Vinegar is an **aqueous solution** that contains ethanoic acid.

Carboxylic acids

AQA	C3	✓
OCR A	C7	✓
EDEXCEL	C3	✓
WJEC	C3	✓
CCEA	C2	✓

Methanoic acid HCOOH	![structure of methanoic acid: H-C with double bond O and O-H]
Ethanoic acid CH_3COOH	![structure of ethanoic acid]
Propanoic acid C_2H_5COOH	![structure of propanoic acid]

> **KEY POINT**
>
> Carboxylic acids are described as **weak acids**.

They can be identified by adding a few drops of universal indicator to a sample. Carboxylic acids will turn the indicator orange-red. Carboxylic acids react with metal carbonates to produce a salt, water and carbon dioxide.

ethanoic acid + sodium carbonate → sodium ethanoate (salt) + water + carbon dioxide

Carboxylic acids react with alcohols to produce **esters** and water. The reaction is catalysed by strong acids.

ethanoic acid + ethanol ⇌ ethyl ethanoate + water

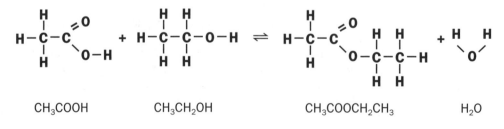

$$CH_3COOH \qquad CH_3CH_2OH \qquad CH_3COOCH_2CH_3 \qquad H_2O$$

Strong and weak acids

AQA	C3	✓
OCR A	C7	✓
EDEXCEL	C3	✓
WJEC	C3	✓

Carboxylic acids are acids because they are proton (hydrogen ion) donors.

> **KEY POINT**
>
> Carboxylic acids are weak because when they are dissolved in water they do not ionise completely. Strong acids such as hydrochloric acid, nitric acid and sulfuric acid completely ionise in water.

The pH of a solution is related to the concentration of hydrogen ions; the higher the concentration of hydrogen ions the lower the pH. So, an aqueous solution of a strong acid (such as hydrochloric acid) will have a higher concentration of hydrogen ions and, therefore, a lower pH than an aqueous solution of a carboxylic acid of the same concentration.

> **PROGRESS CHECK**
>
> 1 What is the name of the functional group found in alcohols?
> 2 What is the molecular formula of propanol?
> 3 How can carboxylic acids be identified?
> 4 What is the general formula of alcohols?
> 5 What are the products of the complete combustion of the alcohol ethanol?
>
> 1. Hydroxyl.
> 2. C_3H_8O.
> 3. Add universal indicator, which will turn orange-red.
> 4. $C_nH_{2n+1}OH$.
> 5. Carbon dioxide and water vapour.

3.7 Analysis

LEARNING SUMMARY

After studying this section, you should be able to:

- Understand the difference between qualitative and quantitative analysis.
- Explain how chromatography can be used to separate and identify substances.
- Explain how infra-red spectroscopy can help identify covalent molecules.
- Explain how gas chromatography and thin-layer chromatography work.
- Describe the use of atomic spectroscopy and mass spectrometry in analysis.

Modern methods of analysis

AQA	C2	✓
OCR A	C7	✓
EDEXCEL	C3	✓
CCEA	C1	✓

Compared to the more traditional laboratory methods, modern instrumental methods of analysing chemicals are:

- faster
- more sensitive
- more accurate and require smaller sample sizes.

Qualitative and quantitative analysis

OCR A	C7	✓
EDEXCEL	C3	✓
CCEA	C1	✓

KEY POINT

Qualitative analysis allows scientists to identify **which components** are present; **quantitative** analysis allows them to decide **how much of each component** is present.

It is important that scientists test a sample that is representative of the whole material being tested and that any sample is collected, stored and prepared carefully to stop any risk of contamination, which would invalidate the results. Many analytical techniques use samples that have been dissolved to form solutions.

Uses of chromatography

AQA	C2	✓
OCR A	C7	✓
EDEXCEL	C2	✓
WJEC	C2	✓
CCEA	C1	✓

Chromatography is used to **separate** out the components of a mixture. It is used to analyse colouring agents in foods, flavourings and drugs. The technique is used in the food industry and by forensic scientists.

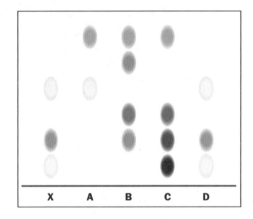

A small spot of the substance being analysed is placed towards the bottom of the chromatography paper. The chromatography paper is then placed into a beaker containing a small amount of the solvent being used. The solvent moves up the paper, carrying the soluble components. When the solvent front reaches the top of the paper, the paper is removed and the solvent is allowed to evaporate. Aqueous solvents contain water and are useful for many ionic compounds. Non-aqueous solvents do not contain water. The more soluble a component is in the solvent the further it will move up the chromatography paper.

R$_f$ values

OCR A	C7	✓
EDEXCEL	C2	✓
WJEC	C2	✓

The **R$_f$ value** is used to compare the distance the component has moved compared to the distance the solvent front has moved.

$$R_f = \frac{\text{distance moved by the component}}{\text{distance moved by the solvent front}}$$

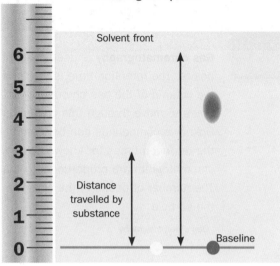

Determining the R_f value

The solvent front has moved 6.0 cm.

The yellow spot has moved 3.2 cm.

The R_f value for the yellow spot $= \frac{3.2 \text{ cm}}{6.0 \text{ cm}} = 0.53$

The green spot has moved 4.8 cm.

The R_f value for the green spot $= \frac{4.8 \text{ cm}}{6.0 \text{ cm}} = 0.8$

If the same solvent and the same conditions are used, the R_f value would be the same for a given component.

> **KEY POINT**
>
> If the R_f value for an unknown compound is determined it can be identified by comparing this value with the R_f values for known compounds.

Unfortunately, similar compounds often have quite similar R_f values.

Infra-red spectroscopy

| WJEC | C3 | ✓ |
| CCEA | C2 | ✓ |

The **infra-red spectroscopy** technique is used to identify the **bonds** present in organic compounds. This allows scientists to suggest the functional groups that are likely to be present. However, all the members of the same homologous series have the same functional group so it can be difficult to identify the exact compound present.

To identify the bonds present, scientists look for peaks at characteristic wavenumbers. C=O bonds are around 1700 cm^{-1}, O-H groups in alcohols are around 3200-3500 cm^{-1} and O-H groups in carboxylic acids are around 2500-3500 cm^{-1}.

> Remember to refer to the wavenumbers for different bonds in your answers.

The breathalyser used by police officers to measure the concentration of alcohol in the breath is based on this technique.

Gas chromatography

AQA	C2	✓
OCR A	C7	✓
WJEC	C2	✓

Gas chromatography is used to identify organic compounds with low boiling points. The retention time is the time that it takes a component to pass through the column of the gas chromatogram. Different components take different times to move through this column and so have different retention times. Unknown compounds can be identified by comparing their retention times with the retention times for known compounds. The areas under the peaks in the chromatogram are proportional to the amount of each compound in the sample. The number of peaks in the chromatogram shows the number of components in the sample.

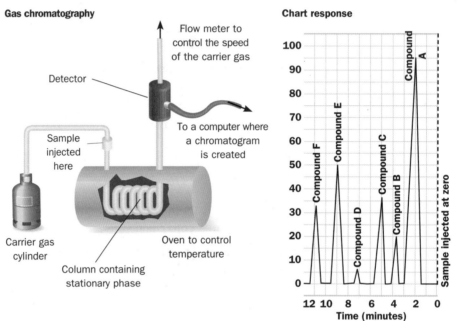

Limitations and uses of gas chromatography

AQA	C2	✓
OCR A	C7	✓
WJEC	C2	✓

Gas chromatography does have some limitations. Many compounds may have similar retention times, so the peaks for some components may be hidden under the peaks identified for other compounds. Also, it cannot be used to identify new compounds as a reference retention time is required to identify the unknown compound. Gas chromatography is a very reliable technique that is often used as evidence in court cases. It can also be used to test for banned substances in an athlete's blood and for pollutants in air or water samples.

Thin layer chromatography

OCR A	C7	✓
OCR B	C3	✓
CCEA	C2	✓

In all types of chromatography, there is a **mobile phase** (the phase that moves) and a **stationary phase** (the phase that does not move). Substances are separated by the movement of the mobile phase through the solid phase. For each component in the mixture there is a dynamic equilibrium between the mobile phase and the solid phase and this is used to separate out the mixture. In **thin layer chromatography** (TLC), the stationary phase is solid and the mobile phase is liquid. This technique is widely used in organic chemistry to check the purity of compounds.

Atomic spectroscopy

| WJEC | C2 | ✓ |

Atomic spectroscopy is used to identify the type and concentration of the atoms or ions present in a sample. For example, if a paint sample from a car was found at a crime scene, forensic scientists could use this technique to identify the make and age of the car involved.

Mass spectrometry

| AQA | C2 | ✓ |
| CCEA | C1 | ✓ |

Mass spectrometry can be used to identify very small samples of material quickly and accurately.

Mass spectrum of ethanol
(C_2H_5OH – relative molecular mass = 46)

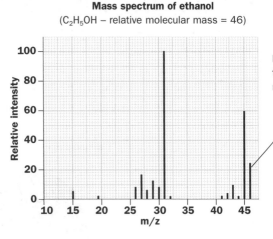

Notice that the peak furthest to the right gives the relative formula mass of the compound (46)

Gas chromatography can be linked to mass spectrometry in a technique known as **GC-MS**. As the sample leaves the gas chromatogram, it is fed into the mass spectrometer and the relative molecular mass of each substance can be identified. The heaviest peak in the sample is known as the molecular ion and can be used to identify the molecular mass of the compound.

PROGRESS CHECK

1. What are the advantages of modern methods of analysis over traditional methods?
2. Why is chromatography useful?
3. What is infra-red spectroscopy used for?
4. Why isn't infra-red spectroscopy used to identify the exact compound present?
5. Chromatography was used to separate a sample of a food colour containing a blue and a green component. The chromatogram produced showed the solvent front moved 8.0 cm while the green component moved 6.0 cm and the blue component moved 5.0 cm. Calculate the Rf values for the green and blue components.

1. They are faster, more sensitive, more accurate, and smaller samples are needed.
2. It is used to separate out the components of a mixture.
3. It identifies the type of bonds present in organic compounds.
4. It identifies bonds but all the members of a homologous series have the same functional group.
5. Green $= \frac{6.0 \text{ cm}}{8.0 \text{ cm}} = 0.75$
   Blue $= \frac{5.0 \text{ cm}}{8.0 \text{ cm}} = 0.625$

3.8 Cosmetics

LEARNING SUMMARY

After studying this section, you should be able to:

- Describe the characteristics of carboxylic acids.
- Recall the uses of esters.
- Explain how a perfume works.
- Understand the key words: solvent, solute and solubility.
- Explain why some substances are soluble in water and some are not.

Carboxylic acids and esters

AQA	C3	✓
OCR A	C7	✓
OCR B	C1	✓
EDEXCEL	C3	✓

Carboxylic acids are a family of organic compounds with the functional group **carboxyl –COOH**. Carboxylic acids are weak acids that react with metals, alkalis and carbonates. They have rather unpleasant smells: they are responsible for the smell of sweaty socks and rancid butter. The well-known carboxylic acid, ethanoic acid, is found in **vinegar**, which can be used to flavour food or as a preservative.

Examples of carboxylic acids

Esters are a family of organic compounds formed when alcohols react with carboxylic acids. Esters have pleasant fruity smells and flavours. Esters are also used as **solvents** and as **plasticisers**.

The ester ethyl ethanoate is formed when ethanol is reacted with ethanoic acid using an acid **catalyst**. Esters are very useful chemicals. Esters are described as being **volatile** because they **evaporate** easily. They are used as cheap alternatives to naturally occurring compounds in perfumes and body sprays, and as flavourings in foods such as yoghurts.

Perfumes

AQA	C3	✓
OCR A	C7	✓
OCR B	C1	✓
EDEXCEL	C3	✓

Traditional perfumes contain plant and animal extracts, such as rose and musk. Today, cheaper, **synthetic** fragrances, including esters, are often used. These are alternatives to materials made from living things. A good perfume should:

- evaporate easily from the skin so that the particles can be smelt
- be **non-toxic**
- not react with water (so it does not react with sweat)
- not irritate the skin (so it does not damage the skin)
- be **insoluble** in water (so it is not washed off easily).

Perfumes evaporate because, although there are strong forces of attraction within perfume molecules, there are weaker forces of attraction between perfume molecules. When the perfume is put on the skin, some of the molecules gain enough energy to evaporate. The perfume molecules can then travel through the air and be smelt.

Animal testing

| OCR B | C1 | ✓ |

Cosmetic products, such as perfumes, have to be tested before they can be sold. Using animals to test cosmetics is banned in the UK but live animals are used to test other products such as new medicines.

- Some people are against animal testing. They believe this causes avoidable suffering to animals.
- Other people think that animal testing is the best way to ensure that products are safe to use and that it allows us to develop new medicines that can save lives.

Making solutions

| OCR B | C1 | ✓ |
| EDEXCEL | C3 | ✓ |

A solution is made from a solvent and a solute.

solvent + solute → solution

- The liquid, which does the dissolving, is called the **solvent**.
- The solid, which is dissolved, is called the **solute**.

- The **solution** is the mixture of the solvent and the solute. Solutions do not separate out (**emulsions** do).
- Water is a good solvent for many solids, but not everything dissolves in water; other liquids, like esters, can also be used.

Soluble and insoluble substances

OCR B	C1, C6 ✓
EDEXCEL	C2, C3 ✓
CCEA	C1 ✓

If a substance dissolves in a particular solvent, it is described as **soluble**. Nail varnish is soluble in nail varnish remover.

If a substance does not dissolve in a particular solvent, it is described as **insoluble**. Nail varnish is insoluble in water.

The forces of attraction between particles decide whether or not something will dissolve.

There are strong forces of attraction between water molecules. There are also strong forces of attraction between nail varnish particles. In fact, there are three lots of forces:

- the forces of attraction between water molecules.
- the forces of attraction between nail varnish particles.
- the forces of attraction between water molecules and nail varnish particles.

The first two forces are stronger than the last: nail varnish particles do not intermingle with the water molecules and nail varnish does not dissolve when you wash your hands in water. However, nail varnish can be removed using other solvents.

PROGRESS CHECK

1. What is the liquid that dissolves something called?
2. What is the solid that is dissolved called?
3. What term is used to describe the mixture made when a solid dissolves in a liquid?
4. Why are synthetic molecules used in some perfumes?
5. Why must perfumes evaporate easily?
6. Describe how aftershave can be smelt from the other side of the room in terms of the particles involved and their movement.

1. Solvent.
2. Solute.
3. Solution.
4. They are cheaper than natural ingredients.
5. So they can travel through the air and reach people's noses to be smelt.
6. The aftershave particles evaporate because, although there are strong forces of attraction within aftershave molecules, there are weaker forces of attraction between the aftershave molecules. When the aftershave is put on the skin, some of the molecules gain enough energy to evaporate. The aftershave molecules can then travel through the air and be smelt, even from the other side of the room.

Sample GCSE questions

1 **(a)** Pentane, C_5H_{12}, is a hydrocarbon and a useful fuel.

   (i) What do you understand by the term 'hydrocarbon'? **[1]**

   A hydrocarbon is a compound that contains only the elements hydrogen and carbon.

   (ii) Write a balanced equation for the burning of pentane in air. **[2]**

   $$C_5H_{12} + 8O_2 \rightarrow 5CO_2 + 6H_2O$$

   1 mark for correct products, 1 mark for balancing.

(b) Pentane can exist in three different isomeric forms, one of which has been drawn for you. Draw the displayed formula of each of the other two isomers of pentane. **[2]**

You are given the formula for pentane in the question. Burning always involves a reaction with oxygen, O_2, and hydrocarbons always produce carbon dioxide and water. Even if you can't balance the equation, you should get a mark for showing you know what is produced.

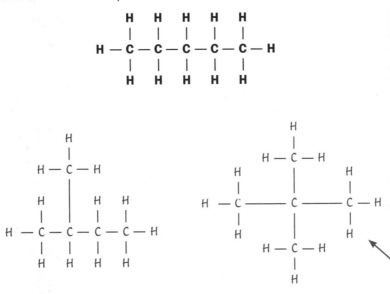

When drawing isomers, just draw the carbon atoms first, showing how they are bonded. Check your isomers are different and only then add the hydrogen atoms. Make sure every carbon has four bonds!

(c) Explain why pentene is not an isomer of pentane. **[2]**

Pentene has a C=C double bond and its formula is C_5H_{10}, so it has two fewer hydrogen atoms.

(d) Describe a test that would allow you to distinguish pentene from pentane, saying how the results would help you to identify the hydrocarbon. **[3]**

The test is to add bromine solution and to shake the mixture. Pentene would turn the bromine solution colourless, pentane would not.

Sample GCSE questions

2 Polytetrafluoroethene, or PTFE, is a man-made polymer. It is produced from the monomer tetrafluoroethene:

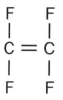

(a) **(i)** What do you understand by the term 'polymer'? **[2]**

A polymer is a long-chain molecule, made from many smaller molecules joined together.

(ii) Write an equation to show the formation of PTFE from tetrafluoroethene. **[2]**

$$n \; \begin{matrix} F & F \\ | & | \\ C = C \\ | & | \\ F & F \end{matrix} \; \longrightarrow \; \left(\begin{matrix} F & F \\ | & | \\ C - C \\ | & | \\ F & F \end{matrix} \right)_n$$

> Remember that the double bond breaks when the polymer forms, so replace it with single bonds.

(iii) What type of polymerisation does this represent? **[1]**

Addition polymerisation

> This is the answer whenever the polymer is the only product.

(b) One property of PTFE is that it has a very low coefficient of friction.

(i) Give one example of a use for PTFE that relies on this property, explaining how it helps. **[2]**

PTFE is used to coat non-stick pans, so that food doesn't stick to them when cooking.

(ii) Is PTFE a thermoplastic or a thermosetting material? Explain how you can tell. **[3]**

It must be thermosetting, otherwise it would soften and melt when heated. It is used on pans which are heated to high temperatures.

Exam practice questions

1 Look at the displayed formulae shown below.

$$H-\underset{\underset{H}{|}}{\overset{\overset{H}{|}}{C}}-\underset{\underset{H}{|}}{\overset{\overset{H}{|}}{C}}-H \qquad \underset{\underset{H}{|}}{\overset{\overset{H}{|}}{C}}=\underset{\underset{H}{|}}{\overset{\overset{H}{|}}{C}} \qquad H-\underset{\underset{H}{|}}{\overset{\overset{H}{|}}{C}}-\underset{\underset{H}{|}}{\overset{\overset{H}{|}}{C}}-O-H$$

Ethane   **Ethene**   **Ethanol**

  (a) Which of the compounds above is an alcohol?   **[1]**

  ....

  (b) Which of the compounds above is unsaturated and would decolourise bromine water?   **[1]**

  ....

  (c) Which of the compounds above could be used to make a plastic through the process of polymerisation?   **[1]**

  ....

  (d) Which of the compounds above could react with a carboxylic acid to form an ester?   **[1]**

  ....

2 Butane and butene are both hydrocarbons.

  (a) What is the chemical formula of butane? .... **[1]**

  (b) Which of the two hydrocarbons is a saturated hydrocarbon? .... **[1]**

  (c) To which series of hydrocarbons does butane belong? .... **[1]**

  (d) Describe a chemical test that would distinguish butane from butene.   **[2]**

  ....

  ....

3 Vegetable oils are used to manufacture soap, in a process known as 'saponification'.

  (a) What sort of chemical is present in vegetable oil?   **[1]**

  ....

  (b) What does the vegetable oil react with, to hydrolyse it?   **[1]**

  ....

  (c) What sort of chemical is a soap molecule?   **[2]**

  ....

  ....

  (d) Give an example of one other industrial use of vegetable oil.   **[1]**

  ....

Exam practice questions

4 Poly(ethene) is made from ethene by a polymerisation reaction.

(a) What happens to the ethene molecules in a polymerisation reaction? **[1]**

....

(b) The formula of ethene is C_2H_4. What is the formula of poly(ethene)? **[1]**

....

(c) Poly(ethene) is a 'thermoplastic' material. What does this mean? **[2]**

....

....

(d) How is high density poly(ethene) structurally different from low density poly(ethene)? **[1]**

....

5 In Brazil, ethanol is produced as a biofuel for cars, to reduce the country's dependency on crude oil.

(a) What is the chemical formula of ethanol? .... **[1]**

(b) What raw material is ethanol made from as a biofuel? .... **[1]**

(c) Write a balanced equation for the fermentation reaction that produces ethanol. **[2]**

....

(d) Why is ethanol a renewable energy resource? **[1]**

....

6 Propanol, C_3H_7OH, is a member of the alcohol family.

(a) What functional group makes propanol an alcohol? .... **[1]**

(b) Why does propanol have a higher boiling point than propane? **[1]**

....

(c) Write a word equation for the complete combustion of propanol. **[2]**

....

(d) Apart from burning as a fuel, what is a likely use for propanol? **[1]**

....

7 Benzene is found in crude oil. It has a boiling point of 81°C. Suggest which of the fractions of crude oil will contain benzene after distillation. Use the information in the table to help you. **[1]**

Fraction	Refinery gases	Petrol	Paraffin/ heating oil	Diesel	Lubricating oil	Fuel oil	Bitumen
Boiling range (°C)	Up to 25	40–100	150–250	220–350	Over 350	Over 400	Over 400

....

Exam practice questions

8 Nail varnish is a substance that is insoluble in water.

(a) Why is it important that nail varnish is insoluble in water? [1]

....

(b) In terms of forces, why is nail varnish insoluble in water? [2]

....

....

(c) What is happening when the nail varnish is drying? [1]

....

(d) Why is it an advantage for the solvent in nail varnish to be volatile? [1]

....

9 The larger the hydrocarbon molecule, the more possible isomers exist.

(a) What do you understand by the term 'isomer'? [2]

....

....

(b) Which is the smallest alkane that can exist as more than one isomer? [1]

....

(c) What is the chemical formula that isomers of this alkane have in common? [1]

....

(d) What type of formula would you have to use to show the difference between isomers? [1]

....

10 **(a)** Crude oil is a mixture of hydrocarbons.

Explain how fractional distillation separates the fractions in crude oil. [2]

....

....

(b) What is cracking and why is it used? [2]

....

....

(c) Explain why small hydrocarbon molecules have a lower boiling point than large hydrocarbon molecules. [2]

....

....

Exam practice questions

11 Margarine is made by hydrogenating vegetable oils, such as sunflower oil.

(a) What important difference does hydrogenation make to the properties of the oil? **[1]**

....

(b) What conditions are required to hydrogenate vegetable oil? **[1]**

....

(c) Vegetable oils are 'unsaturated'. What does this mean? **[1]**

....

(d) How could you demonstrate that a margarine still contained some degree of unsaturation? **[2]**

....

....

12 PVC is a modern polymer material, used to make guttering and water pipes.

(a) From which monomer is PVC made? **[1]**

....

(b) What type of polymerisation happens when PVC is made? **[1]**

....

(c) What advantages do PVC water pipes have over steel pipes? **[2]**

....

....

(d) PVC is a naturally rigid material. What can be added to make it softer? **[1]**

....

13 Ethanol may be used as a fuel and as a solvent. It may be produced by fermenting sugar, using yeast, or by hydrating ethene at high temperature and pressure.

Compare and contrast the cost of production of ethanol by fermentation of sugar with the production by the hydration of ethene.

The quality of written communication will be assessed in your answer to this question. **[6]**

....

....

....

....

....

....

4 Metals and tests

The following topics are covered in this chapter:

- Metals
- Group 1
- Extraction of iron
- Iron and steel
- Aluminium
- Cars
- Transition metals
- Copper
- Chemical tests 1
- Chemical tests 2

4.1 Metals

LEARNING SUMMARY

After studying this section, you should be able to:

- Describe how metal atoms bond together.
- Draw and label a diagram to show metallic bondng and structure.
- Compare the properties of metals with non-metals.
- Understand the term 'shape-memory alloy'.
- Explain how a superconductor works.

Metallic structure

AQA	C2	✓
OCR A	C5	✓
OCR B	C4	✓
EDEXCEL	C2	✓
CCEA	C1	✓

Metals have a giant structure. In metals, the electrons in the highest energy shells (outer electrons) are not bound to one atom but are **delocalised**, or free to move through the whole structure. This means that metals consist of positive metal ions surrounded by a sea of negative electrons. **Metallic bonding** is the attraction between these positive ions and the negative electrons. This is an **electrostatic** attraction.

> Remember, the metallic bond is the electrostatic attraction between the positive metal ions and the delocalised electrons.

Metallic structure

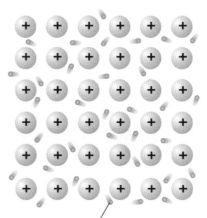

Moving electrons can carry the electric charge or thermal (heat) energy.

Properties of metals

AQA	C2	✓
OCR A	C5	✓
OCR B	C4	✓
EDEXCEL	C2	✓
WJEC	C1, C2	✓
CCEA	C1	✓

Metallic bonding means that metals have several very useful properties:

- The free electrons mean that metals are **good electrical conductors**.
- The free electrons also mean that metals are **good thermal conductors**.
- The strong attraction between the metal ions and the electrons means that metals can be drawn into wires as the ions slide over each other.
- Metals can also be hammered into shape.
- Most have **high melting points** because lots of energy is needed to overcome the strong metallic bonds.

> **Remember to say that metals conduct electricity because the delocalised electrons can move. Do not talk about atoms or ions moving.**

Non-metals

WJEC	C1, C2	✓
CCEA	C1	✓

Non-metals are found on the right-hand side of the periodic table. They tend to be **poor electrical and thermal conductors**. Non-metals generally have **low melting points** and boiling points and are sometimes gases at room temperature.

Smart alloys

AQA	C2	✓
OCR B	C2	✓
EDEXCEL	C1	✓
WJEC	C2	✓

Smart alloys are new materials with amazing properties. One famous example of a smart alloy is **nitinol**. Nitinol is an alloy of nickel and titanium. Some smart alloys have a shape memory. When a force is applied to a smart alloy it **stretches**. When a smart alloy is heated up, however, it returns to its original shape.

Smart alloys appear to have a **shape memory** because they are able to exist in two solid forms. A temperature change of 10–20 degrees is enough to cause smart alloys to change forms. Shape-memory polymers behave in a similar way, returning to their original shape when heated. At low temperatures, smart alloys exist in their low temperature form.

If a force is applied to the alloy it can be distorted to the low temperature, deformed form of the alloy.

When the alloy is heated, it changes to the higher temperature form.

In shape-memory alloys, the low temperature form and the high temperature form are the same shape and size, so when they are heated smart alloys appear to have a shape memory. Nitinol is used in some dental braces.

Superconductors

OCR B	C4	✓

Some metals can behave as **superconductors** at very low temperatures. Metals can conduct electricity because they have delocalised electrons that can move. Metals normally have a **resistance** to the current that is flowing. Energy is lost as the current overcomes this resistance and the metal warms up.

Superconductors are special because they have **little or no resistance**. The advantages of using superconductors include:

- If there is no resistance then no energy is lost when a current flows.
- As the resistance decreases the current can flow faster, so super-fast circuits can be developed.
- They can be used to make powerful electromagnets.

Despite these advantages, superconductors are not widely used because they only work below a **critical temperature**. Although this varies for different superconductors, the current critical temperatures are around −170°C; until they work at room temperature, their use is likely to be limited.

PROGRESS CHECK

1. What is metallic bonding?
2. Why are metals good electrical conductors?
3. Which metals are used to make nitinol?
4. Why do metals have high melting points?
5. Give a use of nitinol.
6. Why is the use of superconductors limited at present?

1. Metallic bonding is the attraction between the positive metal ions and the sea of negative, delocalised electrons.
2. They have delocalised electrons that can move.
3. Nickel and titanium.
4. A lot of energy is required to overcome the metallic bonds.
5. Nitinol is used in some dental braces.
6. Superconductors only work below their critical temperatures; at present these temperatures are too low to be readily attainable.

4.2 Group 1

LEARNING SUMMARY

After studying this section, you should be able to:

- Recall the characteristic properties of group 1 elements.
- Write equations for reactions between a group 1 element and water.
- Explain why elements in the same group react in a similar way.
- Explain the increase in reactivity as you go down group 1.
- Describe trends in physical properties of group 1 elements.

The group 1 metals

AQA	C3	✓
OCR A	C4	✓
OCR B	C4	✓
EDEXCEL	C2	✓
WJEC	C2, C3	✓
CCEA	C1	✓

The **elements** in group 1, on the far left-hand side of the periodic table, are known as the **alkali metals**. They are soft metals with fairly **low melting points**.

Rubidium and caesium belong to group 1, but are too **reactive** for use in schools. As alkali metals get more reactive they react more vigorously with water. Alkali metals are so reactive that they must be stored under oil to prevent them reacting with moisture or oxygen. Alkali metals are shiny when freshly cut, but they tarnish quickly as they react with oxygen. Gloves and goggles should be worn when using alkali metals.

Alkali metals have **low densities** – lithium, sodium and potassium are all less dense than water. The alkali metals become denser down the group. When alkali metal atoms react they lose the single electron in their outermost shell to form ionic compounds in which the alkali metal ions have a 1+ charge. For example:

$Na \rightarrow Na^+ + e$

KEY POINT
The alkali metals react with water to form strongly **alkaline hydroxide** solutions and hydrogen gas.

metal + water $\rightarrow$ metal hydroxide + hydrogen

> To get a top grade, you need to be able to write the symbol equations to sum up these three reactions.
>
> $2Li + 2H_2O \rightarrow 2LiOH + H_2$
> $2Na + 2H_2O \rightarrow 2NaOH + H_2$
> $2K + 2H_2O \rightarrow 2KOH + H_2$

Metal	Observations when metal reacts with water	Equation
Lithium, Li	Metal floats on water. Some bubbles seen.	Lithium + Water $\rightarrow$ Lithium Hydroxide + Hydrogen
Sodium, Na	Metal forms a molten ball that moves around on the surface of the water. Many bubbles seen.	Sodium + Water $\rightarrow$ Sodium Hydroxide + Hydrogen
Potassium, K	The metal reacts even more vigorously than sodium (it can ignite). Lots of bubbles are seen and the metal burns with a lilac flame.	Potassium + Water $\rightarrow$ Potassium Hydroxide + Hydrogen

Why group 1 metals all react in a similar way

AQA	C2, C3	✓
OCR A	C4	✓
OCR B	C4	✓
EDEXCEL	C1	✓
WJEC	C2	✓
CCEA	C1	✓

Alkali metals have just one electron in their outer shell and have similar properties because they have similar electron structures. Alkali metals react with non-metals to form ionic compounds. For example, sodium reacts with chlorine to form sodium chloride.

sodium + chlorine $\rightarrow$ sodium chloride

When sodium is burned, it reacts with oxygen to form sodium oxide.

sodium + oxygen $\rightarrow$ sodium oxide

> To get a top grade, you need to be able to write the symbol equations to sum up these reactions.
>
> $2Na + Cl_2 \rightarrow 2NaCl$
> $4Na + O_2 \rightarrow 2Na_2O$

When they react, an alkali metal atom loses its outer electron to form ions with a 1+ charge.

$Na \rightarrow Na^+ + e^-$

The alkali metal atom has lost an electron so it is **oxidised**. Alkali metals form solid white ionic compounds that dissolve to form colourless solutions.

The further down the group the further the outer electron is from the nucleus. Further down the group there are more shells shielding the outer electron from the atom's nucleus, so it is easier for atoms to lose their outer electron.

Melting and boiling points of group 1 metals

AQA	C3	✓
OCR A	C4	✓
WJEC	C1	✓

Melting and boiling points decrease down the group. Alkali metals are held together by metallic bonding. Metallic bonding is the attraction between the positive metal ions and the 'sea' of negative electrons.

The atoms get larger down the group, so the strength of the metallic bonding decreases. As the forces of attraction become weaker down the group it takes less energy to overcome these forces so the alkali metals will melt and boil at lower temperatures.

PROGRESS CHECK

1. Name the first three metals in group 1.
2. How many electrons are present in the outer shell of all group 1 metals?
3. Why do all the group 1 metals have similar properties?
4. What type of compounds do group 1 metals form?
5. Potassium reacts with chlorine to produce the compound potassium chloride.
   a) Write a word and symbol equation to sum up this reaction.
   b) Is the potassium oxidised or reduced in this reaction? Explain your answer.

b) $K \rightarrow K^+ + e^-$. Potassium has lost an electron so it is oxidised in this reaction.

$2K \quad + Cl_2 \quad \rightarrow 2KCl$

5. a) potassium + chlorine → potassium chloride

4. Ionic compounds.

1+.

3. They have the same outer electron structure.

2. One.

1. Lithium, sodium and potassium.

4.3 Extraction of iron

LEARNING SUMMARY

After studying this section, you should be able to:

- Explain why displacement reactions occur.
- Understand the role of carbon in the extraction of iron from its ore.
- Write equations to represent the reactions happening in a blast furnace.
- Understand the terms 'oxidation' and 'reduction'.
- List the raw materials that are used in the blast furnace.

Methods of extracting metals

AQA	C1	✓
OCR A	C5	✓
OCR B	C2	✓
EDEXCEL	C1	✓
WJEC	C1	✓
CCEA	C2	✓

Metals are very useful materials but they are normally found combined with other elements in **compounds** in the Earth's crust. The more **reactive** a metal is, the harder it is to remove it from its compound.

Gold is so **unreactive** that it is found uncombined, but most other metals are found in compounds. Occasionally, rocks are found that contain metals in such high concentrations that it is economically worthwhile to extract the metal from the rock. Such rocks are called **ores**. The ores are **mined**. The metals can be **extracted** using **chemical reactions**. The exact method chosen depends on the reactivity of the metal and the purity of the metal required.

Displacement reactions

AQA	C1	✓
OCR A	C5	✓
OCR B	C6	✓
EDEXCEL	C1	✓
WJEC	C1	✓
CCEA	C2	✓

In **displacement** reactions, a more reactive metal takes the place of a less reactive metal. Iron is more reactive than copper so if an iron nail is placed in a solution of blue copper(II) sulfate the nail changes colour from silver to pink-orange and the solution turns pale. There is also a slight temperature rise.

The more reactive metal, iron, displaces the less reactive metal, copper, from a solution of its compound.

iron + copper(II) sulfate → iron(II) sulfate + copper

The balanced symbol equation for this displacement reaction is:

$Fe + CuSO_4 \rightarrow FeSO_4 + Cu$

The iron atoms are oxidised while the copper ions are reduced.

In a similar way, copper will displace silver from a solution of silver nitrate. The copper atoms are oxidised while the silver ions are reduced.

copper + silver nitrate → copper nitrate + silver
$Cu \quad + 2AgNO_3 \quad \rightarrow Cu(NO_3)_2 \quad + 2Ag$

In **competition** reactions, a metal is heated with the metal oxide of a less reactive metal. If iron is heated with copper(II) oxide the more reactive metal, iron, removes the oxygen from the less reactive metal, copper.

iron + copper(II) oxide → iron(II) oxide + copper
Fe + CuO → FeO + Cu

Extracting iron

AQA	C1	✓
EDEXCEL	C1	✓
WJEC	C1	✓
CCEA	C2	✓

Iron is an **element**. Elements are substances that are made of only one type of atom. There are only about 100 different elements. Iron is an extremely important metal. It is extracted from iron ore in a **blast furnace**. Iron is less reactive than carbon. Iron can be extracted from iron oxide by reducing the metal oxide with carbon.

The blast furnace

| WJEC | C1 | ✓ |
| CCEA | C2 | ✓ |

The solid **raw materials** in the blast furnace are iron ore and coke (a source of the element carbon) and limestone (which reacts with impurities). A fourth raw material, the gas air, is also used. The main ore of iron is **haematite**. This ore contains the compound iron(III) oxide, Fe_2O_3.

Blast furnace

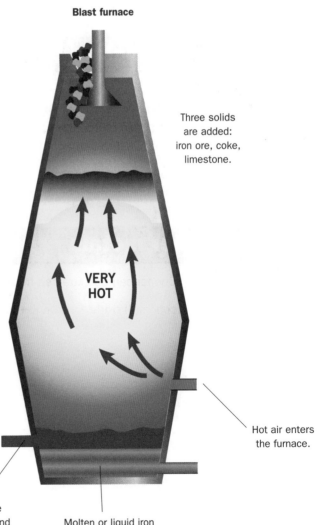

Three solids are added: iron ore, coke, limestone.

VERY HOT

Hot air enters the furnace.

Slag (limestone impurities) is found on top of the iron.

Molten or liquid iron is found at the bottom.

4 Metals and tests

- Hot air is blasted into the furnace. The oxygen in the air reacts with the carbon in the coke to form carbon dioxide and release energy.

  carbon + oxygen → carbon dioxide
  $C(s) + O_2(g) → CO_2(g)$

- At the very high temperatures inside the blast furnace, carbon dioxide reacts with more carbon to form carbon monoxide.

  carbon dioxide + carbon → carbon monoxide
  $CO_2(g) + C(s) → 2CO(g)$

- The carbon monoxide reacts with iron oxide to form iron and carbon dioxide.

  carbon monoxide + iron oxide → iron + carbon dioxide
  $3CO(g) + Fe_2O_3(s) → 2Fe(l) + 3CO_2(g)$

Haematite contains many impurities including substantial amounts of **silicon dioxide** (**silica**). Limestone is added to the blast furnace because it reacts with these silica impurities to form **slag**. Slag has a low density and floats to the top of the iron ore where it can be removed. Slag is used in road building and in the manufacture of fertilisers.

Owing to the high temperatures in the blast furnace, the iron that is made is a liquid. This molten iron is dense and sinks to the bottom of the furnace where it can be removed. Iron ore is mainly reduced by the gas carbon monoxide but some is reduced by carbon.

Oxidation and reduction in the extraction of iron

AQA	C1	✓
OCR A	C1	✓
OCR B	C6	✓
WJEC	C1	✓
CCEA	C2	✓

In many examples, oxygen is gained in **oxidation** reactions and oxygen is lost in **reduction** reactions. Oxidation and reduction always happen together. During the extraction of iron the carbon is first oxidised to carbon monoxide. The iron oxide is reduced to iron and the carbon monoxide is oxidised to carbon dioxide.

Corrosion is an example of an oxidation reaction. The less reactive a metal is the more slowly it corrodes.

Extracting other metals

AQA	C1	✓
EDEXCEL	C1	✓
CCEA	C2	✓

Copper can be extracted from copper oxide by heating it with carbon.

copper(II) oxide + carbon → copper + carbon dioxide

PROGRESS CHECK

1. What happens in a displacement reaction?
2. What colour is copper(II) sulfate solution?
3. Give the word equation for the reaction between copper sulfate and iron.
4. Zinc is more reactive than copper. Write the word and symbol equations to sum up the reaction between zinc metal and copper(II) sulfate solution. Which metal is oxidised and which metal is reduced in this reaction?

The zinc is oxidised and the copper is reduced.
$Zn + CuSO_4 \longrightarrow ZnSO_4 + Cu$
4. zinc + copper(II) sulfate $\longrightarrow$ zinc(II) sulfate + copper
3. iron + copper(II) sulfate $\longrightarrow$ iron(II) sulfate + copper
2. Blue.
1. A more reactive metal takes the place of a less reactive metal.

4.4 Iron and steel

LEARNING SUMMARY

After studying this section, you should be able to:

- Describe the problems caused by the rusting of iron and steel.
- Compare the different ways that iron and steel can be protected against rusting.
- Explain how alloying can alter the properties of a metal.
- Understand the differences between cast iron, wrought iron and steel.
- Relate the properties of different steels to their uses.

Preventing iron from rusting

OCR B	C2, C6	✓
EDEXCEL	C1	✓
CCEA	C2	✓

Iron **corrodes**, or **rusts**, faster than most other **transition metals**.

KEY POINT

Rusting involves **oxidation**. It requires the presence of both oxygen and water and produces hydrated iron(III) oxide.

Rusting is accelerated by salt water and by acid rain. Iron can be prevented from rusting by completely removing it from contact with either oxygen or water.

iron + oxygen + water $\rightarrow$ hydrated iron(III) oxide

Oxidation and reduction reactions always involve **electrons**.

KEY POINT

In oxidation reactions electrons are always lost. In reduction reactions electrons are always gained.

In this example, the iron is oxidised and oxygen is reduced. The iron is the reducing agent and the oxygen is the oxidising agent.

Coating the iron

Painting or **coating** iron in plastic, oil or with tin plate can stop oxygen and water from reaching the metal. If the coating is damaged, however, the iron will start to rust.

Tin is less reactive than iron. If the tin is scratched, the iron will react by losing electrons, even faster than it would normally do, so the iron will rust more quickly.

Sacrificial protection

Sacrificial protection involves placing iron in contact with a more reactive metal like zinc or magnesium to prevent rusting. The iron is protected because the more reactive metal reacts by losing electrons, instead of the iron – which is why the method is called sacrificial protection. **Galvanising** protects iron by coating it in a layer of zinc, another sacrificial metal. The zinc layer stops oxygen and water from reaching the iron.

Alloying the metal

AQA	C1	✓
OCR B	C2, C6	✓
EDEXCEL	C1	✓
WJEC	C1	✓
CCEA	C1	✓

Alloys are mixtures containing one or more metal. They are made by mixing molten mixtures of metals together. Most **pure metals**, such as copper and aluminium, are too soft for many uses so molten mixtures of similar metals are combined to form alloys. Pure metals have layers because all the atoms are the same size and these atoms can pass over each other.

> **KEY POINT**
>
> In alloys the atoms are different sizes; this causes disruption of the layers so they cannot pass over each other. Alloys are much harder and so much more useful, such as brass, bronze, steel, solder and amalgam.

Cast iron and wrought iron

| AQA | C1 | ✓ |
| OCR B | C2 | ✓ |

The iron that is made in a blast furnace contains large amounts of the element carbon. If this iron is allowed to cool down and solidify, it forms **cast iron**. Cast iron contains about 96% pure iron and is used to make objects like drain covers. It is hard, strong and does not rust. Cast iron does have one notable disadvantage: it is brittle and can crack easily.

Wrought iron

Wrought iron is made by removing the impurities from cast iron. It is much softer than cast iron and is used to make objects like gates.

Wrought iron is softer and easier to shape than cast iron because of its structure. It is made from almost pure iron. The iron atoms form a very regular arrangement. The layers of iron atoms are able to slip easily over each other.

Wrought iron structure

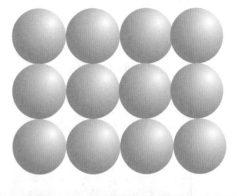

Steel

AQA	C1	✓
OCR B	C2, C4	✓
EDEXCEL	C1	✓

Most of the iron made in the blast furnace is used to produce steel. Mixing iron with other metals and carbon to form alloys, such as stainless steel, will also protect the metal. To make steel:

- Any carbon impurities must first be removed from the iron, to produce pure iron.
- Other metals and carefully controlled amounts of the non-metal element carbon are added to the iron.

Steel is much harder than wrought iron because it consists of atoms of different elements. These atoms are different sizes and cannot pack together to form a regular structure. This irregular structure makes it very difficult for layers of atoms to slide over each other, which makes the steel very hard.

By carefully controlling the amount of carbon that is added to steel, scientists can produce a metal that has exactly the right properties for each particular job:

Steel structure

Low carbon steels are soft and easy to shape. Objects such as car bodies are made from low carbon steels.

- **Medium carbon steels** are harder, stronger and less easy to shape. Objects such as hammers are made from medium carbon steels.
- **High carbon steels** are hard, strong, brittle and hard to shape. Objects such as razor blades are made from high carbon steels.
- **Iron** can also be alloyed with other metals to form different types of steel.

Stainless steel is a very widely used alloy. It consists of 70% iron, 20% chromium and 10% nickel. Stainless steel is extremely resistant to corrosion.

PROGRESS CHECK

1. What must be present for iron to rust?
2. Give the chemical name for rust.
3. What are alloys?
4. A sample of pure silver was found to be too soft for making jewellery. Explain how the silver could be made more hard-wearing in terms of the atoms involved.

4. The silver should be alloyed with another metal to make it harder. Pure metals have layers because all the atoms are the same size and these layers can pass over each other. In alloys the atoms are different sizes; this causes disruption of the layers so they cannot pass over each other.
3. Alloys are mixtures containing one or more metal.
2. Hydrated iron(III) oxide.
1. Water and oxygen.

4.5 Aluminium

LEARNING SUMMARY

After studying this section, you should be able to:

- Recall the properties and uses of aluminium.
- Understand the use of electrolysis in extracting aluminium from its ore, bauxite.
- Understand the role of cryolite in the electrolysis.
- Describe what happens at each electrode in the electrolytic cell.
- Use the terms 'oxidation' and 'reduction' to categorise the discharging of ions.

Bauxite

| WJEC | C1 | ✓ |
| CCEA | C2 | ✓ |

Aluminium is abundant in the Earth's crust, but it is also very **reactive** and so it is much harder to **extract** from its **ores**. Consequently, aluminium is more expensive than iron.

The main ore of aluminium is called **bauxite**. Bauxite contains the compound aluminium oxide, Al_2O_3. Unfortunately, bauxite is often found in environmentally sensitive areas such as the Amazonian rainforests. Extracting bauxite from these places brings jobs and money to the area, but can also scar the landscape and harm local wildlife. New roads can damage the areas around the mines and local people can be displaced by the development.

Recycling aluminium

AQA	C1	✓
WJEC	C1	✓
CCEA	C2	✓

One way to protect the areas where bauxite is found is for people to simply **recycle** their old aluminium cans. Recycling has many advantages. It means that:

- Less bauxite will need to be extracted.
- Landfill sites will not be filled up with discarded aluminium cans.
- Much less energy is used by recycling than extracting aluminium straight from its ore.

Properties and uses of aluminium

AQA	C1	✓
EDEXCEL	C1	✓
WJEC	C1	✓
CCEA	C1, C2	✓

Although pure aluminium is quite **soft**, when it is alloyed with other metals it becomes much stronger. Aluminium alloys combine high strength with low density. This makes aluminium a very useful metal for producing objects like aeroplanes and mountain bikes. It is also a good electrical conductor.

Aluminium is a reactive metal and yet it is widely used to make drinks cans. Aluminium is much less reactive than its position in the reactivity series would suggest. This is because when aluminium objects are made their surfaces quickly react with oxygen to form a thin layer of **aluminium oxide**. This layer stops the aluminium metal from coming into contact with other chemicals and so prevents any further reaction. The layer of aluminium oxide means that it is quite safe to drink fizzy, acidic drinks from aluminium cans.

Aluminium reacts with oxygen to form aluminium oxide

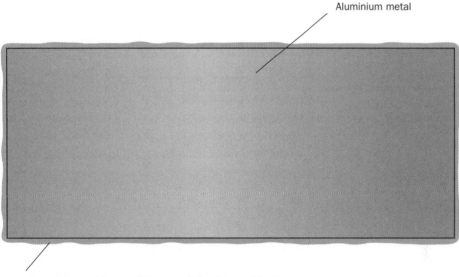

Aluminium metal

Layer of aluminium oxide   The layer of aluminium oxide stops aluminium from reacting further.

The extraction of aluminium

AQA	C1	✓
OCR A	C5	✓
EDEXCEL	C1	✓
WJEC	C1	✓
CCEA	C2	✓

> **KEY POINT**
>
> Aluminium is more reactive than carbon and so it is extracted using **electrolysis**, even though this is a very expensive method.

For electrolysis to occur, the aluminium ions and oxide ions in bauxite must be able to move. This means that the bauxite has to be either heated until it melts or dissolved in something.

Bauxite has a very **high melting point** and heating the ore to this temperature is very expensive. Fortunately, another ore of aluminium, called **cryolite**, has a much lower melting point. First, the cryolite is heated up until it melts and then the bauxite is dissolved in the molten cryolite. Extracting aluminium from its ore requires a lot more **energy** than extracting iron from its ore.

Electrolysis of molten aluminium oxide

AQA	C1, C2	✓
OCR A	C5	✓
EDEXCEL	C1	✓
WJEC	C1	✓
CCEA	C2	✓

Electrolysis of bauxite (aluminium oxide)

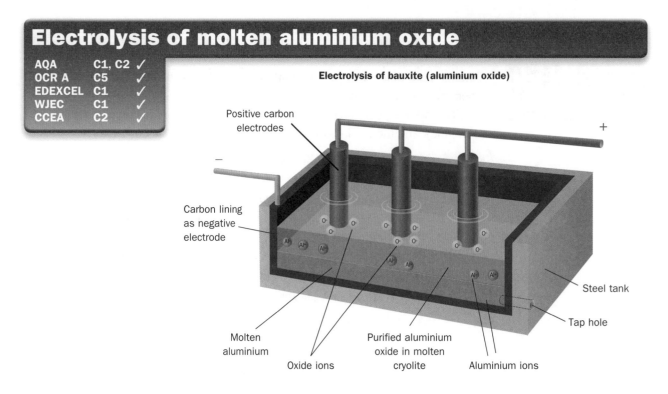

Positive carbon electrodes

Carbon lining as negative electrode

Steel tank

Tap hole

Molten aluminium

Oxide ions

Purified aluminium oxide in molten cryolite

Aluminium ions

Aluminium can now be extracted by electrolysis. By dissolving the aluminium oxide, both the aluminium, Al^{3+} and the oxide, O^{2-} ions can move. During electrolysis, the aluminium, Al^{3+} ions are attracted to the negative electrode (the cathode) where they pick up electrons to form aluminium Al atoms. The aluminium metal collects at the bottom of the cell where it can be gathered.

aluminium ions + electrons → aluminium atoms
$$Al^{3+} + 3e^- \rightarrow Al$$

The oxide, O^{2-} ions are attracted to the positive electrode (the anode) where they deposit electrons to form oxygen molecules.

oxide ions → oxygen molecules + electrons
$$2O^{2-} \rightarrow O_2 + 4e^-$$

The oxygen that forms at the positive electrode readily reacts with the carbon, graphite electrode to form carbon dioxide. The electrodes, therefore, must be replaced periodically. Extracting aluminium is expensive because lots of energy is required and because there are lots of stages in the process.

> To get a top grade, make sure you can write equations for the reactions taking place at the electrodes.
> $Al^{3+} + 3e^- \rightarrow Al$
> $2O^{2-} - 4e^- \rightarrow O_2$

Oxidation and reduction in electrolysis

AQA	C2	✓
OCR A	C5	✓
EDEXCEL	C1	✓
WJEC	C1	✓
CCEA	C2	✓

In the electrolysis of aluminium oxide:

- Aluminium ions are reduced to aluminium atoms.
- Oxide ions are oxidised to oxygen molecules.

Reduction reactions happen when a species gains electrons. In this case, each aluminium ion gains three electrons to form an aluminium atom.

Oxidation reactions occur when a species loses electrons. In this case, two oxide ions both lose two electrons to form an oxygen molecule.

Reduction and oxidation reactions must always occur together and so are sometimes referred to as **redox** reactions.

> Oxidation and reduction can be remembered using the mnemonic <u>OIL</u> <u>RIG</u>:
> <u>O</u>xidation <u>I</u>s <u>L</u>oss
> <u>R</u>eduction <u>I</u>s <u>G</u>ain (of electrons).

PROGRESS CHECK

1 What is the name of a mixture of metals?
2 What is the formula of aluminium oxide?
3 What is the name of the method used to extract aluminium from its ore?
4 In the extraction of aluminum, why is bauxite dissolved in molten cryolite?

4. Bauxite has a very high melting point and the addition of cryolite reduces this temperature and, therefore, the energy needed.
3. Electrolysis.
2. Al_2O_3.
1. An alloy.

4.6 Cars

LEARNING SUMMARY

After studying this section, you should be able to:

- Compare advantages and disadvantages of aluminium and steel as construction materials.
- Describe the advantage of using hydrogen as a fuel for cars.
- Explain how a fuel cell works.
- Write equations for the chemical reactions happening in a fuel cell.
- Explain the advantage a fuel cell has over traditional methods of producing electricity.

Choosing between aluminium and steel

OCR B   C2   ✓

Cars have become an indispensable part of many people's lives. However, cars do not last forever and their disposal can cause problems. Cars are built using a wide range of different materials.

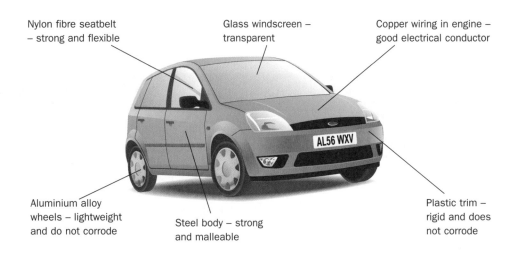

Nylon fibre seatbelt – strong and flexible

Glass windscreen – transparent

Copper wiring in engine – good electrical conductor

AL56 WXV

Aluminium alloy wheels – lightweight and do not corrode

Steel body – strong and malleable

Plastic trim – rigid and does not corrode

Steel and aluminium can both be used as construction materials. Iron and aluminium are both extracted from their ores, which are found in the Earth's crust. Although both these materials are metals they have different properties:

- Steel is magnetic while aluminium is non-magnetic.
- Steel is denser than aluminium.
- Steel corrodes readily while aluminium does not. Conditions affect how quickly metals corrode. Acid rain, salt water and moist air all increase the rate of corrosion.

Like all metals, both iron and aluminium are good **electrical** and **thermal conductors**. They are both **malleable** and can be hammered into shape; this is particularly useful for making cars.

Car bodies have traditionally been made from steel. However, some cars are now being built from aluminium. New laws will soon mean that a certain minimum amount of any new car must be recyclable.

Advantages of building cars from steel	Advantages of building cars from aluminium
Steel is cheaper than aluminium, so steel cars will be cheaper to buy.	Aluminium cars do not corrode so aluminium cars will last longer.
	Aluminium is less dense than steel so aluminium cars will be lighter than steel cars. Aluminium cars will have a better fuel economy.

> Learn the information in this table.

Hydrogen as a fuel

OCR B	C6	✓
EDEXCEL	C1	✓
WJEC	C1	✓
CCEA	C2	✓

Hydrogen can be used as a **fuel**. When it burns it reacts with oxygen to form water. The reaction is **exothermic**. The hydrogen burns with a clean blue flame.

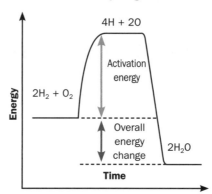

Fuel cells

AQA	C3	✓
OCR B	C6	✓
EDEXCEL	C1	✓

Fuel cells are a very efficient way of producing electrical energy. Most fuel cells use hydrogen, but other fuels, such as ethanol, can be used. Typically, hydrogen and oxygen are fed into the fuel cell and chemical reactions inside the cell produce electricity.

Traditionally, **fossil fuels** like petrol have been used as a fuel for cars. However, these fuels have many disadvantages:

- They are **non-renewable**.
- When they are burned they release carbon dioxide, which is thought to contribute towards the **greenhouse effect**.

Fuel cells could also be used to power cars. If hydrogen was used, the cars would not produce carbon dioxide and, as the hydrogen is made by the decomposition of water, an effectively limitless amount of hydrogen gas could be made.

However, the use of **fuel cells** can still cause pollution. Many fuel cells contain poisonous **catalysts** that must be removed from the cell before it is disposed of. In addition, although the fuel cell itself does not produce carbon dioxide, water is currently decomposed to form hydrogen and oxygen using electricity that has been generated by burning fossil fuels – a process that does produce carbon dioxide.

Advantages of fuel cells

| AQA | C3 | ✓ |
| OCR B | C6 | ✓ |

Fuel cells are ideal for remote situations where space is limited; they have been used to power spacecraft. Hydrogen fuel cells produce water, which is non-polluting and is essential for the astronauts. The fuel cells are also **lightweight** and small. As they have no moving parts, fuel cells are unlikely to break down and are very efficient. Traditional methods of producing electricity, for example in coal-fired power stations, involve many more stages. This makes them less efficient; older methods also produce more pollution.

A fuel cell produces electrical energy.

In a typical fuel cell, a fuel such as hydrogen reacts with oxygen to create a potential difference. Hydrogen is added at the anode. The hydrogen molecules lose electrons to form hydrogen ions.

$$2H_2 \rightarrow 4H^+ + 4e^-$$

Oxygen is added at the cathode.

$$O_2 + 4H^+ + 4e^- \rightarrow 2H_2O$$

The hydrogen ions produced at the anode move through the electrolyte to the cathode where they join with oxygen and electrons to form water.

Overall:

hydrogen + oxygen → water
$$2H_2 + O_2 \rightarrow 2H_2O$$

PROGRESS CHECK

1. Which factors increase the rate at which iron rusts?
2. Why do cars made from aluminium last longer than cars made from steel?
3. Name the product made when hydrogen is burned in oxygen.
4. Why is hydrogen considered to be a non-polluting fuel?
5. Write the word and symbol equations for the overall reaction inside a typical fuel cell.

5. hydrogen + oxygen → water
$2H_2 + O_2 \rightarrow 2H_2O$
4. When it burns, hydrogen only produces water, which is non-polluting.
3. Water.
2. Aluminium does not corrode.
1. Acid rain, salt water and moist air all increase the rate of corrosion.

4.7 Transition metals

LEARNING SUMMARY

After studying this section, you should be able to:

- Show where transition metals are found on the Periodic Table.
- Recall the properties of a typical transition metal.
- Relate the properties of transition metals to their uses.
- Describe the stages involved in the production of titanium.
- Relate the properties of titanium to specific uses.

Properties and reactions of transition metals

AQA	C1, C3	✓
OCR B	C4	✓
EDEXCEL	C2	✓

Transition metals are found in the middle section of the periodic table. Copper, iron and nickel are examples of very useful transition metals.

> **KEY POINT**
>
> All transition metals have characteristic properties:
>
> - High **melting points** (except for mercury, which is a liquid at room temperature).
> - A high **density**.
>
> There are **coloured compounds**:
>
> - Copper(II) compounds are blue or green.
> - Iron(II) compounds are green.
> - Iron(III) compounds are a 'foxy' red.

Transition metals are also strong, tough, good thermal and electrical conductors, malleable and hard wearing. All transition metals are much less reactive than group 1 metals. They react much less vigorously with oxygen and water. Many transition metals can form ions with different charges. This makes transition metals useful catalysts for many reactions.

Titanium

| AQA | C1 | ✓ |

Despite being very abundant in the Earth's crust, **titanium** is an expensive metal. This is because it is difficult to extract titanium from its ore. The main ore of titanium is **rutile**. Rutile contains the compound titanium oxide, TiO_2. Titanium is more reactive than carbon and so cannot be extracted simply by heating titanium oxide with carbon.

The extraction of titanium is quite a complicated process:

- First, the titanium oxide is converted to titanium chloride.
- Next, the titanium chloride is reacted with molten magnesium. Magnesium is more reactive than titanium and a chemical reaction takes place in which titanium is displaced.

titanium chloride + magnesium → titanium + magnesium chloride

The **extraction** of titanium involves many steps and requires a lot of **energy**, so it is very **expensive**.

Properties of titanium

| AQA | C1 | ✓ |
| WJEC | C1 | ✓ |

Titanium has some very special properties:

- It is very strong and hard when **alloyed** with other metals.
- It has a very **low density**.
- It is easy to shape.
- It has a very high melting point.
- It is very resistant to **corrosion**.

Titanium appears to be **unreactive** because the surface of titanium objects quickly reacts with oxygen to form a layer of titanium oxide. This layer prevents any further reaction taking place.

Titanium's properties mean that this metal is very useful. Titanium alloys are used to make:

- replacement hip and elbow joints
- aircraft
- rockets and missiles.

Other useful metals

AQA	C1	✓
OCR B	C4, C6	✓
EDEXCEL	C1	✓
WJEC	C1	✓
CCEA	C1	✓

Copper has some very special properties:

- It is a good **thermal** and **electrical conductor**.
- It is easy to shape.
- It is very **unreactive** – even with water.
- It has an attractive colour and lustre.
- It is very resistant to **corrosion**.

Copper's properties mean that it is a very useful metal. Copper is used to make water pipes and tanks, saucepans, and electrical wires.

Copper has many uses

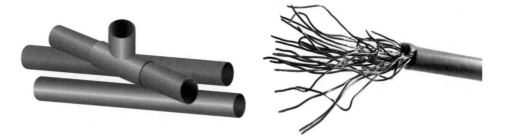

Iron made in the **blast furnace is strong but brittle**. Iron is often made into steel. **Steel** is strong and cheap and is used in vast quantities, but it is also heavy and may rust. Iron and steel are useful structural materials. They are used to make buildings, bridges, ships, cars and trains. Iron is used as a **catalyst** in the **Haber process**.

Gold is used to make jewellery and electrical components. Gold is a highly valued metal that has an attractive colour and lustre. It is also a good thermal conductor and, because of its low reactivity, is very resistant to corrosion. Pure gold is too soft for many uses so it is usually mixed with other metals to form alloys. The **carat scale** and the **fineness scale** are both used to show the amount of pure gold in the alloy; in both cases, the higher the number the greater the proportion of gold.

> Make sure you can suggest some uses for these different metals

Nickel is used as a **catalyst** in the manufacture of margarine.

Common metal alloys

| AQA | C1 | ✓ |
| OCR B | C2 | ✓ |

Common alloys include:

- Amalgams which are mainly mercury.
- Brass which is made from copper and zinc.
- Bronze which is made from copper and tin.
- Solder which is made from lead and tin.
- Steel which is mainly iron.

PROGRESS CHECK

1. In which section of the periodic table are the transition metals found?
2. Why is copper used for electrical wiring and for water pipes?
3. In which process is iron used as a catalyst?
4. How can you tell how pure a sample of gold is?
5. Why are many transition metal compounds useful catalysts?
6. Give the word equation for the displacement reaction between titanium chloride and magnesium.
7. Why is the extraction of titanium very expensive?

7. It involves lots of steps and requires lots of energy.
6. titanium chloride + magnesium → titanium + magnesium chloride
5. Many transition metals can form ions with different charges.
4. Use the carat scale or the fineness scale.
3. The Haber process.
2. It is a good electrical conductor that can be shaped.
1. The middle section.

4.8 Copper

LEARNING SUMMARY

After studying this section, you should be able to:

- Describe how copper may be extracted from copper carbonate and from copper oxide.
- Understood the terms 'bioleaching' and 'phytomining' in copper extraction.
- Explain the purification of copper by electrolysis.
- Write equations for the reactions occurring at the electrodes in copper purification.
- Explain why copper is often alloyed with other metals to improve its properties.

Extraction of copper

AQA	C1	✓
OCR A	C5	✓
OCR B	C2	✓

Copper is an unreactive metal that has several ores. It has been known since ancient times, so the richest supplies of ores have been exhausted. Copper is now extracted from rocks that do not contain large amounts of the metal. This means that a lot of rock has to be **quarried** in order to extract enough copper which can cause significant damage to the local area.

Copper sometimes is found uncombined (or native) in nature. The mineral malachite contains copper carbonate, $CuCO_3$. When it is heated, the copper carbonate breaks down to form copper oxide and carbon dioxide.

copper carbonate → copper oxide + carbon dioxide

$$CuCO_3 \rightarrow CuO + CO_2$$

The copper oxide produced reacts with carbon to form copper and carbon dioxide.

copper oxide + carbon → copper + carbon dioxide

$$2CuO + C \rightarrow 2Cu + CO_2$$

Extracting copper from low-grade ores

| AQA | C1 | ✓ |

Scientists are developing ways to exploit copper from **low-grade ores**, which contain copper at lower concentrations than would normally be economically worthwhile to use. The idea is to leach copper out of the ores to form a solution then extract the copper from the solution using electrolysis or by displacement with scrap Iron.

Metals can be extracted from low-grade ores using plants. As the plant grows, it takes up the metal, which accumulates in the plant's biomass. When the plant is harvested the biomass can be burned to produce a bio-ore. This process, called **phytomining**, allows scientists to exploit ores that had previously been uneconomic to use.

Bioleaching is the process of extracting metals from their ores using **bacteria**. Advantages of bioleaching include:

- It is a simpler and cheaper process compared to traditional smelting methods.
- It causes less damage to the landscape than traditional methods.

Disadvantages of bioleaching include:

- It is a very slow process.
- There is a risk of pollution if toxic chemicals are allowed to escape into the environment.

Phytomining allows scientists to recover toxic metals from waste dumps and to reclaim **contaminated** areas of land. The recovered metals, such as nickel and cobalt, can be used for new purposes. The land can also be converted to new uses, such as agriculture or for building new homes.

KEY POINT

Recycling copper is better for the environment because fewer raw materials are needed. As less energy is required, the copper is cheaper to buy.

However, people have to be persuaded to recycle their waste metals rather than putting them into landfill sites. Sorting waste metals can also be very labour intensive and expensive.

Purification of copper

AQA	C1	✓
OCR A	C5	✓
OCR B	C2, C4,	✓
	C6	✓
EDEXCEL C3		✓

Copper must be purified before it can be used for some applications, such as high-specification wiring. Copper is purified using electrolysis.

Electrolysis of copper

Positive electrode

Negative electrode

This electrode dissolves.

Pure copper forms here.

Cu^{2+}

Cu^{2+}

Sludge formed from impurities

Copper sulfate solution

- During the electrolysis of copper, the impure copper metal is used as the positive electrode where the copper atoms give up electrons to form copper ions.
- As the positive electrode dissolves away, any impurities fall to the bottom of the cell to form sludge.
- Copper ions in the solution are attracted towards the negative electrode where the copper ions gain electrons to form copper atoms.
- The positive electrode gets smaller while the negative electrode gets bigger. In addition, the negative electrode is covered in very pure copper.

Electrode reactions during copper purification

AQA   C1   ✓
OCR B   C2, C6 ✓
EDEXCEL   C3   ✓

To get a top grade, you should be able to write word and symbol equations for the reactions that take place at the electrodes.

The reaction at the positive electrode:

copper atoms → copper ions + electrons

$$Cu \rightarrow Cu^{2+} + 2e^-$$

The reaction at the negative electrode:

Copper ions + electrons → Copper atoms

$$Cu^{2+} + 2e^- \rightarrow Cu$$

Copper alloys

OCR B   C2   ✓
WJEC   C1   ✓

Pure copper is too soft for many uses. In pure copper the atoms are all the same size and so they form a regular arrangement. Copper is soft because the layers of atoms can pass easily over each other. Copper is often mixed with other metals to form **alloys**.

Bronze is made by mixing copper and tin. It is much harder than either copper or tin and consists of different sized atoms, so the atoms cannot pack together to form a regular structure. Bronze is hard because the layers of atoms cannot pass easily over each other. The invention of bronze was a major advance: it was used to make stronger tools and weapons.

PROGRESS CHECK

1. What method is used to purify copper?
2. If you wanted to coat a metal object with copper, which electrode should you attach it to?
3. Copper can be purified by electrolysis.
   a) Give the symbol equation for the reaction that takes place at the positive electrode during the purification of copper.
   b) Give the symbol equation for the reaction that takes place at the negative electrode during the purification of copper.

1. Electrolysis.
2. The negative electrode.
3. a) $Cu \rightarrow Cu^{2+} + 2e^-$.
   b) $Cu^{2+} + 2e^- \rightarrow Cu$.

4.9 Chemical tests 1

LEARNING SUMMARY

After studying this section, you should be able to:

- Recall the gas tests for carbon dioxide, hydrogen, chlorine, oxygen and ammonia.
- Describe how to carry out a flame test.
- Link the flame test colour to the presence of certain metal ions.
- Link hazard symbols to their meanings.
- Describe the purposes of a number of useful separation techniques.

Gas tests

OCR B	C1, C2,	✓
	C4, C6	✓
EDEXCEL	C1, C2	✓
WJEC	C1, C3	✓
CCEA	C1, C2	✓

Chemists use these tests to identify the following common gases:

Carbon dioxide: The gas is bubbled through limewater. The limewater turns cloudy. Carbonates react with acids to produce carbon dioxide.

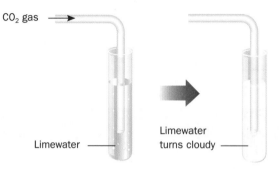

CO_2 gas →

Limewater

Limewater turns cloudy

Hydrogen: A lighted splint is placed nearby. The hydrogen burns with a squeaky pop. The flame goes out.

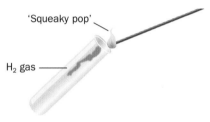

'Squeaky pop'

H_2 gas

Chlorine: Place damp litmus paper in the gas. The litmus paper is bleached.

Damp litmus paper

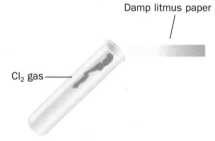

Cl_2 gas

Make sure you are familiar with the tests for common gases – you will need to state the reagents used and the results in the exam.

Oxygen: A glowing splint is placed in the gas. The splint relights.

Glowing splint

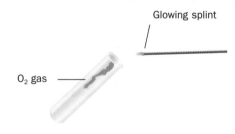

O_2 gas

Ammonia: Place damp red litmus paper in the gas. The damp red litmus paper turns blue.

NH_3 gas

Damp red litmus

Flame tests

AQA	C3	✓
OCR A	C4	✓
OCR B	C4	✓
EDEXCEL	C2	✓
WJEC	C2, C3	✓
CCEA	C1	✓

Flame tests can be used to identify some metals present in salts. These elements give distinctive flame colours when heated because the light given out by a particular element gives a characteristic **line spectrum**. The technique of **spectroscopy** has been used by scientists to discover new elements, including caesium and rubidium. What do you do?

- Clean a flame test wire by placing it into the hottest part of a Bunsen flame.
- Dip the end of the wire into water and then into the salt sample.
- Hold the salt in the hottest part of the flame and observe the colour seen.

> For flame tests, give the name of the metal responsible for a colour, not the name of a whole compound.

Metal ion present	Colour in flame test
Lithium	Crimson
Sodium	Yellow/orange
Potassium	Lilac
Calcium	Red
Barium	Light green
Copper	Blue/green

Hazard symbols

OCR A	C4, C6	✓
EDEXCEL	C1, C2	✓
CCEA	C1	✓

Hazard symbols are a very effective way of alerting people to the dangers associated with different chemicals.

Toxic These substances can kill. They can act when you swallow them, breathe them in or absorb them through your skin. *Example: chlorine gas.*		**Corrosive** These substances attack other materials and living tissue, including eyes and skin. *Example: concentrated sulfuric acid.*	
Oxidising These substances provide oxygen, which allows other substances to burn more fiercely. *Example: hydrogen peroxide.*		**Irritant** These substances are not corrosive but they can cause blistering of the skin. *Example: calcium chloride.*	
Harmful These substances are similar to toxic substances but they are less dangerous. *Example: lead oxide.*		**Explosive** These substances are explosive. *Example: urea nitrate.*	
Highly Flammable These substances will catch fire easily. They pose a serious fire risk. *Example: hydrogen.*			

> Questions are often asked about hazard symbols. Make sure you can identify what each symbol shows and explain what it means.

Useful techniques in science

OCR A	C6, C7	✓
CCEA	C1	✓

- **Dissolving** is used to form a solution from a soluble solute and a suitable solvent.
- **Crystallisation** is used to produce solid crystals from a solution.
- **Filtration** is used to separate an insoluble solid from a mixture.
- **Evaporation** is used to turn a liquid into a gas. If a solution is evaporated to dryness the mass of the solute can be found.
- **Drying**, in an oven or in a desiccator, is used to remove water from a sample.

PROGRESS CHECK

1. What are the tests for carbon dioxide, hydrogen, chlorine and oxygen?
2. Which scientific technique is used to separate an insoluble solid from a mixture?
3. Describe how you would carry out a flame test.

3. First, clean a flame test wire by placing it into the hottest part of a Bunsen flame. Next, dip the end of the wire into water and then into the salt sample. Finally, hold the salt in the hottest part of the flame and observe the colour seen.
2. Filtration.
Oxygen relights a glowing splint.
Chlorine bleaches damp litmus paper.
Hydrogen burns with a squeaky pop.
1. When carbon dioxide is bubbled through limewater it turns the limewater cloudy.

4.10 Chemical tests 2

LEARNING SUMMARY

After studying this section, you should be able to:

- Understand how the formula of an ionic compound can be deduced from the charges of the ions.
- Describe how to carry out a test for halide ions and interpret the test result.
- Describe how to carry out a test for sulfate ions and interpret the test results.
- Describe how carbonates can be identified.
- Describe the use of sodium hydroxide to identify metal ions in solution.

Formulae of ionic compounds

AQA	C3	✓
OCR A	C4–C7	✓
OCR B	C1–C6	✓
EDEXCEL	C2	✓
WJEC	C1	✓
CCEA	C1	✓

Metal ions	Non-metal ions
Sodium, Na^+	Oxide, O^{2-}
Magnesium, Mg^{2+}	Chloride, Cl^-
Calcium, Ca^{2+}	Bromide, Br^-
Potassium, K^+	Hydroxide, OH^-
Iron(II), Fe^{2+}	Nitrate, NO_3^-
Iron(III), Fe^{3+}	Carbonate, CO_3^{2-}
Copper(II), Cu^{2+}	Sulphate, SO_4^{2-}

The compound magnesium oxide contains magnesium, Mg^{2+}, and oxide, O^{2-}, ions. For every one magnesium ion, one oxide ion is required. The overall formula for the compound is MgO.

Testing for halide ions

AQA	C3	✓
OCR B	C4, C5	✓
EDEXCEL	C2, C3	✓
WJEC	C2, C3	✓
CCEA	C1	✓

It is important that a test for a particular ion gives a result that is **unique** to that ion for a positive identification to be made. These tests are very important and are used to check for the presence of chemicals in blood and to check the purity of drinking water.

Identifying halide ions			
Halide ion	Test	Results	Ionic half equations
Chloride, Cl^-	Add dilute nitric acid then **silver nitrate** solution	Chloride ions give a white precipitate of silver chloride.	$Ag^+(aq) + Cl^-(aq) \rightarrow AgCl(s)$
Bromide, Br^-	Add dilute nitric acid then **silver nitrate** solution	Bromide ions give a cream precipitate of silver bromide.	$Ag^+(aq) + Br^-(aq) \rightarrow AgBr(s)$
Iodide, I^-	Add dilute nitric acid then **silver nitrate** solution	Iodide ions give a yellow precipitate of silver iodide.	$Ag^+(aq) + I^-(aq) \rightarrow AgI(s)$

Testing for sulfate ions

AQA	C3	✓
OCR B	C5	✓
EDEXCEL	C2	✓
WJEC	C3	✓
CCEA	C1	✓

To test for the presence of sulfate ions in solution:

- Add barium chloride solution.
- Then add dilute hydrochloric acid.

A white precipitate of barium sulfate shows that sulfate ions are present in the original solution.

barium chloride + sodium sulfate → barium sulfate + sodium chloride

Symbol equation:

$$BaCl_2(aq) + Na_2SO_4(aq) \rightarrow BaSO_4(s) + 2NaCl(aq)$$

Ionic equation:

$$Ba^{2+}(aq) + SO_4^{2-}(aq) \rightarrow BaSO_4(s)$$

Identifying carbonates

AQA	C2, C3	✓
OCR A	C3, C6	✓
OCR B	C2	✓
EDEXCEL	C1	✓
WJEC	C1	✓
CCEA	C1	✓

Metal **carbonates** react with dilute hydrochloric acid to form a salt, water and carbon dioxide gas. To prove the gas produced is carbon dioxide, place a drop of limewater (calcium hydroxide $Ca(OH)_2$ solution) on a glass rod. If carbon dioxide is present the limewater turns cloudy.

When copper(II) carbonate is heated it decomposes to form copper(II) oxide and carbon dioxide. This can be identified by a distinctive colour change: copper carbonate is green and copper oxide is black.

copper carbonate + hydrochloric acid → copper chloride + water + carbon dioxide

Symbol equation:

$CuCO_3(s) + 2HCl(aq) \rightarrow CuCl_2(aq) + H_2O(l) + CO_2(g)$

Ionic equation:

$CuCO_3(s) + 2H^+(aq) \rightarrow Cu^{2+}(aq) + H_2O(l) + CO_2(g)$

Hydroxide tests

| AQA | C3 | ✓ |
| OCR B | C4 | ✓ |

Dilute **sodium hydroxide** solution can be used to test for the presence of some transition metal ions in solution. The sodium hydroxide solution is added drop-wise to the solution of the transition metal compound. The colour of the precipitate formed is used to identify the transition metal ion.

Transition metal ion	Results
Copper(II), Cu^{2+}	Blue precipitate of copper(II) hydroxide, $Cu(OH)_2$.
Iron(II), Fe^{2+}	Green precipitate of iron(II) hydroxide, $Fe(OH)_2$. This quickly darkens as the Fe^{2+} ions are oxidised to Fe^{3+} ions.

Sodium hydroxide can also be used to identify aluminium and calcium ions in solutions.

Metal ion	Results
Aluminium, Al^{3+}	White precipitate that *does* dissolve in excess sodium hydroxide to form a colourless solution.
Calcium, Ca^{2+}	White precipitate that does *not* dissolve in excess sodium hydroxide.

To test for the presence of **ammonium ions** in a compound, add sodium hydroxide solution and then warm the resulting mixture. Then test for the presence of ammonia gas.

PROGRESS CHECK

1. What is the test for the gas carbon dioxide?
2. What colour is the precipitate formed when copper(II) ions react with hydroxide ions?
3. What colour is the precipitate formed when iron(II) ions react with hydroxide ions?
4. Give the ionic equation for the reaction between copper(II) carbonate and hydrochloric acid.

4. $CuCO_3(s) + 2H^+(aq) \rightarrow Cu^{2+}(aq) + H_2O(l) + CO_2(g)$
3. Green.
2. Blue.
1. It turns limewater cloudy.

Sample GCSE questions

1. Rohin had some of a white solid that he knew was a salt of some sort. He decided to analyse the salt to find out what it was.

    (a) (i) Rohin started his analysis by carrying out a flame test. Describe what he had to do, to carry out this test. **[3]**

    He should clean a nichrome wire by dipping it into hydrochloric acid. He should then dip the wire into the salt. He should place the wire in the hottest part of a roaring Bunsen burner flame and should note what colour the flame turned.

    (ii) Rohin found that the salt gave a lilac flame. What does this tell him? **[2]**

    The salt contains potassium.

    ← The salt is not potassium itself, which is a metal. Learn flame colours!

    (b) Rohin took some of the salt and dissolved it in water. He added some nitric acid and then a few drops of silver nitrate solution.

    (i) What was Rohin testing for? **[1]**

    He was testing to see if the salt was a halide.

    ← Learn these chemical tests!

    (ii) If Rohin's test proved negative, which three types of compound can be ruled out? **[3]**

    He can rule out chloride, bromide and iodide from the possible identity of the salt.

    (c) Rohin added some barium chloride to his salt solution and a white precipitate formed immediately. What is the identity of the salt he was testing? **[1]**

    Potassium sulfate.

    ← Note you are being asked for the full name of the salt.

Sample GCSE questions

2 Aluminium is extracted from its ore, bauxite, using electrolysis.

Carbon lining as negative electrode

carbon anodes

+

−

Steel tank

Tap hole

Molten aluminium

bauxite in molten cryolite

(a) (i) Add the two labels that are missing from the diagram. **[2]**

(ii) Why is it not possible to reduce the aluminium oxide in bauxite using carbon? **[2]**

Aluminium is more reactive than carbon. Carbon cannot displace aluminium from a compound.

(b) Aluminium is a more reactive element than iron, but it does not corrode as much.

(i) Explain why aluminium is more resistant to corrosion than iron. **[2]**

An oxide layer forms on the surface which protects the metal.

(ii) Apart from resistance to corrosion, why might it be an advantage to make a boat from aluminium instead of steel? **[3]**

Aluminium has a lower density than steel, so it will make the boat lighter. The boat will require less energy to move through the water.

Notice that there are three marks, so the question obviously expects either more than one answer or a fully explained answer.

Exam practice questions

1 In metals the outer-shell electrons of the atoms are 'delocalised'.

(a) What does 'delocalised' mean? **[1]**

....

(b) Explain what holds the atoms together in metallic bonding. **[2]**

....

....

(c) What property of metals relies upon the electrons being able to move? **[1]**

....

2 Sodium metal reacts vigorously with water, producing a flammable gas, which sometimes ignites.

(a) Which gas is produced when sodium reacts with water? **[1]**

....

(b) What other product is made in this reaction? **[1]**

....

(c) Write a balanced symbol equation for the reaction. **[2]**

....

3 The main ore of iron is haematite: its formula is Fe_2O_3. Iron may be extracted from haematite in a blast furnace.

(a) What is an 'ore'? **[2]**

....

....

(b) Which element displaces iron from its oxide in the blast furnace? **[1]**

....

(c) What is the main impurity in the haematite? **[1]**

....

4 Explain why the method used to extract aluminium from its oxide is different from that used to extract iron from its oxide. **[4]**

....

....

....

....

Exam practice questions

5 **(a)** Steel is an alloy composed mainly of iron. Explain why steel is more useful for making support cables in bridges than iron. **[2]**

....

....

(b) Name the metal that is mixed with lead to make solder. **[1]**

....

(c) Give two properties that make solder useful for welding metal gas pipes together. **[2]**

....

6 Electrolysis is used to extract aluminium from bauxite.

(a) In this process, what is produced at the negative electrode (cathode)? **[1]**

....

(b) What is produced at the positive electrode (anode)? **[1]**

....

(c) What is the bauxite dissolved in and why? **[2]**

....

....

(d) Why is production of aluminium an expensive process? **[1]**

....

7 A car body panel made from aluminium will never rust, so it should last longer than a traditional car body panel.

(a) Which alloy has traditionally been used to make car body panels? **[1]**

....

(b) Give one advantage, other than not rusting, that an aluminium panel gives. **[1]**

....

(c) Give one disadvantage of making car body panels out of aluminium. **[1]**

....

(d) Explain how making car bodies out of aluminium makes recycling cars easier. **[2]**

....

....

Exam practice questions

8 Gold is a dense, unreactive metal that is soft and easy to shape.

(a) Where, on the periodic table, is gold found? **[1]**

....

(b) What properties of gold make it suitable for making jewellery? **[2]**

....

....

(c) Which cheaper metal is gold often alloyed with to improve its hardness? **[1]**

....

(d) What name is given to the purity rating scale of gold? **[1]**

....

9 A car manufacturer is investing a large amount of money to develop cars that don't rely on fossil fuels. One possibility is to power the car using electricity. Another possibility is to use hydrogen as a fuel.

(a) Describe the most important environmental advantage that hydrogen has over fossil fuels. **[1]**

....

(b) Describe two ways in which hydrogen-fuelled cars can still cause pollution. **[2]**

....

....

10 Flame tests are used in the chemical analysis of salts.

(a) What can be identified by carrying out a flame test? **[1]**

....

(b) If a salt produces a yellow flame, what does that show? **[1]**

....

(c) Why might it be easy to confuse copper salts with barium salts? **[1]**

....

(d) Why must the wire be cleaned before each flame test? **[2]**

....

....

Exam practice questions

11 Testing for the three different halide ions involves adding the same reagent to each, after first acidifying the solution with nitric acid.

(a) What is the reagent used to test for halide ions? **[1]**

....

(b) What result shows a halide is present? **[1]**

....

(c) What is the difference between the result for a chloride and for a bromide? **[2]**

....

....

(d) Write an equation for the reaction between silver ions, Ag^+, and chloride ions, Cl^-. **[1]**

....

12 Nitinol is described as a 'smart alloy'. It is a metal with unusual properties.

(a) Which two metallic elements combine to make nitinol? **[2]**

....

....

(b) What happens to a piece of nitinol when a large force is applied to it? **[1]**

....

(c) Why might nitinol be useful for spectacle frames? **[1]**

....

13 Fuel cells produce electricity from the reaction between hydrogen and oxygen. They may power cars in the future.

What advantages would a fuel cell have over a petrol or diesel engine?

The quality of written communication will be assessed in your answer to this question. **[6]**

....

....

....

....

....

....

5 Acids, bases and salts

The following topics are covered in this chapter:

- Acids and bases
- Making salts
- Limestone
- Metal carbonate reactions
- The electrolysis of sodium chloride
- Titrations
- Water and solubility
- Hard and soft water

5.1 Acids and bases

LEARNING SUMMARY

After studying this section, you should be able to:

- Explain the difference between a strong acid and a weak acid.
- Relate the strength of an acid to its uses.
- Explain the difference between a strong alkali and weak alkali.
- Use the pH scale as a measure of acidity or alkalinity.
- Recognise the property that makes indicators useful.

Strong acids

AQA	C3	✓
OCR A	C7	✓
OCR B	C2, C5	✓
EDEXCEL	C1	✓
WJEC	C1, C3	✓
CCEA	C1	✓

Acids and **bases** are chemical **opposites**. Some bases dissolve in water and are called **alkalis**.

Acidic solutions have a **pH** less than 7. **Acidic compounds** can be solids like citric acid or tartaric acid, liquids like sulfuric acid, nitric acid or ethanoic acid or gases like hydrogen chloride.

Some acids are described as **strong**. Examples of strong acids include hydrochloric acid, which is produced in the stomach and helps break down food and kills bacteria, sulfuric acid and nitric acid.

Strong acids are completely **ionised** in water. When hydrochloric acid is placed in water, every hydrogen chloride molecule splits up to form hydrogen ions and chloride ions.

$$HCl \rightarrow H^+ + Cl^-$$

Weak acids

AQA	C3	✓
OCR A	C7	✓
OCR B	C2, C5	✓
WJEC	C1, C3	✓
CCEA	C1	✓

Other acids are described as **weak acids**. Examples of weak acids include ethanoic acid, citric acid and carbonic acid.

Weak acids do not completely ionise in water. When ethanoic acid is placed in water, only a small fraction of the ethanoic acid molecules split up to form hydrogen ions and ethanoate ions.

> Acids are proton donors. Bases are proton acceptors.

$$CH_3COOH \rightleftharpoons H^+ + CH_3COO^-$$

Notice that this reaction is **reversible**. Ethanoic acid reacts more slowly with metals, alkalis and carbonates than a comparative amount of a strong acid like hydrochloric acid would do. This is because ethanoic acid produces fewer H^+ ions and so there are fewer collisions between reactant particles and H^+ ions.

A sample of a weak acid, like ethanoic acid, has a lower conductivity than a sample of a strong acid, like hydrochloric acid, because hydrochloric acid is fully **dissociated** (that is, split up) in water and produces more H^+ ions to carry charge.

However, both acids would produce the same volume of carbon dioxide if they were reacted with calcium carbonate or magnesium carbonate.

Weak acids, such as vinegar, are widely used as descalers since they remove limescale without damaging the surface of the object being cleaned.

Concentrated sulfuric acid is a dehydrating agent and can be used to remove water from sugar and from hydrated copper sulfate.

Weak and strong alkalis

AQA	C3	✓
OCR A	C3, C6	✓
OCR B	C2	✓
WJEC	C1	✓
CCEA	C1	✓

Traditional sources of alkalis included stale urine and burned wood. With **industrialisation**, the demand for alkalis grew, so shortages of alkalis soon developed.

Alkalis were used to **neutralise** acid soils, to produce the chemicals needed to bind dyes to cloth, to convert fats and oils into soap and to manufacture glass. Early methods of manufacturing alkalis from limestone and salt produced a lot of **pollution**, including the acid gas hydrogen chloride and waste heaps that slowly released the toxic and unpleasant smelling gas hydrogen sulfide. **Oxidation** of hydrogen chloride forms chlorine gas.

Alkaline solutions have a pH more than 7.

> **KEY POINT**
>
> Some alkalis are described as **strong alkalis**. Examples of strong alkalis include sodium hydroxide and potassium hydroxide.

> Hydroxide ions have the formula OH⁻. Remember to add the negative charge. Strong alkalis have a high pH and are fully ionised.

Strong alkalis are completely ionised in water. When sodium hydroxide is placed in water, it splits up to form sodium ions and hydroxide ions.

$$NaOH \rightarrow Na^+ + OH^-$$

> **KEY POINT**
>
> Other alkalis are described as weak. Ammonia is an example of a **weak alkali**.

Weak alkalis do not completely ionise in water. Ammonia produces hydroxide, OH^-, ions when it reacts with water.

ammonia + water $\rightleftharpoons$ ammonium ion + hydroxide ion

$$NH_3 + H_2O \rightleftharpoons NH_4^+ \qquad + OH^-$$

Ammonium salts are useful **fertilisers**.

The pH scale

AQA	C2	✓
OCR A	C6	✓
OCR B	C2, C5	✓
WJEC	C1	✓
CCEA	C1	✓

The pH scale can be used to distinguish between weak and strong acids and alkalis. The pH scale measures the concentration of hydrogen ions. Neutral solutions have a pH of 7. Acidic solutions have a pH of less than 7.

The strongest acids have a pH of 1. Dilute solutions of weak acids have higher pH values than dilute solutions of strong acids. Many foods, such as lemons, contain acids. These foods taste sour. If water is added to an acid it becomes more dilute and less corrosive. Alkaline solutions have a pH of more than 7. The strongest alkalis have a pH of 14. Many cleaning materials contain alkalis. If water is added to an alkali it becomes more dilute and less corrosive.

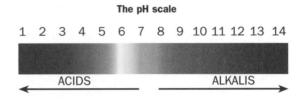

The pH scale

1 2 3 4 5 6 7 8 9 10 11 12 13 14

ACIDS   ALKALIS

Indicators

AQA	C3	✓
OCR A	C6	✓
OCR B	C2, C5	✓
EDEXCEL	C3	✓
CCEA	C1	✓

Indicators can be used to show the pH of a solution. Indicators work by changing colour. They can show when exactly the right amount of acid and alkali have been added together. Red litmus turns blue in alkaline conditions while blue litmus turns red in acidic conditions.

PROGRESS CHECK

1. Which ions are found in acidic solutions?
2. Which ions are found in alkaline solutions?
3. Name three strong acids and explain why they are described as 'strong'.
4. A 1 g sample of calcium carbonate was placed in 50 cm³ of 1.0 mol dm⁻³ ethanoic acid. An identical sample of calcium carbonate was then placed in 50 cm³ of 1.0 mol dm⁻³ hydrochloric acid.
   a) In what ways would the reactions be the same?
   b) In what ways would the reactions be different?

4. a) Both reactions would produce carbon dioxide/bubbles would be seen/the same volume of gas would be made in both experiments.
   b) The reaction involving hydrochloric acid would be faster because it is a strong acid while ethanoic acid is a weak acid.
3. Hydrochloric acid, sulfuric acid and nitric acid. They are completely ionised in water.
2. OH⁻ ions.
1. H⁺ ions.

149

5.2 Making salts

LEARNING SUMMARY

After studying this section, you should be able to:

- Explain neutralisation, using the ionic equation for the formation of water.
- Predict what type of salt will be produced when using a given acid.
- Recall that metal salts are made from metals or from metal oxides with acids.
- Understand what is shown by a pH curve for a neutralisation reaction.
- Describe how insoluble salts are prepared by precipitation reactions.

Neutralisation reactions

AQA	C2	✓
OCR A	C3, C6	✓
OCR B	C2, C5	✓
EDEXCEL	C1	✓
WJEC	C1	✓
CCEA	C1	✓

The reaction between an acid and a base is called **neutralisation**.

- Acidic solutions contain hydrogen, H^+ ions.
- Alkaline solutions contain hydroxide, OH^- ions.

The reaction between an acid and an alkali can be shown in a word equation:

acid + alkali → salt + water

The ionic equation for all neutralisation reactions is:

$$H^+(aq) + OH^-(aq) \rightarrow H_2O(l)$$

The type of salt that is produced during the reaction depends on the acid and the alkali used. Indigestion medicines contain chemicals that react with, and neutralise, excess stomach acid.

Naming salts

AQA	C2	✓
OCR A	C6	✓
OCR B	C2	✓
EDEXCEL	C1	✓
WJEC	C1	✓
CCEA	C1	✓

Neutralising hydrochloric acid will produce **chloride salts**.

hydrochloric acid + sodium hydroxide → sodium chloride + water

Neutralising nitric acid will produce **nitrate salts**.

nitric acid + potassium hydroxide → potassium nitrate + water

Neutralising sulfuric acid will produce **sulfate** salts.

sulfuric acid + sodium hydroxide → sodium sulfate + water

Ammonia reacts with water to form a weak alkali. Ammonia solution can be neutralised with acids to form **ammonium salts**.

Making salts from metal oxides

AQA	C2	✓
OCR A	C6	✓
OCR B	C2	✓
EDEXCEL	C1	✓
CCEA	C1	✓

Metal oxides are also bases. They can be reacted with acids to make salts and water:

| metal oxide | + acid | → salt | + water |

copper(II) oxide + hydrochloric acid → copper(II) chloride + water

$$Cu \quad + 2HCl \quad \rightarrow CuCl_2 \quad + H_2O$$

zinc oxide + sulfuric acid → zinc sulfate + water

$$ZnO + H_2SO_4 → ZnSO_4 + H_2O$$

pH curves

OCR B   C5   ✓

The diagram below can be used to analyse what happens to the pH as acids and alkalis react together.

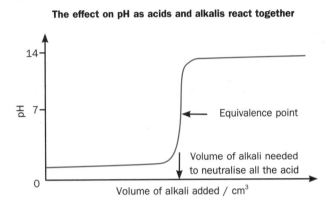

The effect on pH as acids and alkalis react together

In this experiment, 25 cm^3 of 0.1 mol dm^{-3} of the strong acid hydrochloric acid was placed in a flask and the pH was taken using a **pH meter**. A 0.1 mol dm^{-3} solution of the alkali sodium hydroxide was placed in a burette. A small amount of the alkali was added to the flask containing the acid and the new pH was recorded. This was repeated until all the alkali had been added.

At first, as the alkali is added the pH changes very little as there is a large excess of the strong acid. Nearer to the **equivalence point** (when exactly the right amount of alkali has been added to react with all the acid) the pH increases more quickly.

Eventually there is a very sharp increase in pH as a tiny amount of alkali is added. The equivalence point is the middle of this vertical part of the graph. The graph shows the volume of alkali needed to react with all the acid from the x axis. As more alkali is added the pH increases slightly as the alkali is now in excess.

> **KEY POINT**
>
> It is necessary to choose an indicator that changes colour suddenly over the vertical part of the graph; **phenolphthalein** changes colour between 8.5 and 10.0.

At a low pH it is colourless; at higher pH it is pink. pH curves can also be drawn for acids being added to alkalis.

Making salts from metals

AQA   C2   ✓
OCR A   C6   ✓
EDEXCEL   C1   ✓
WJEC   C1   ✓
CCEA   C1   ✓

Fairly reactive metals can be reacted with acids to form a salt and hydrogen. Salts of very unreactive metals, such as copper, cannot be made in this way because these metals do not react with acids.

Salts of very reactive metals, such as sodium, cannot be made in this way because the reaction between the metal and acid is too vigorous to be carried out safely.

Precipitation reactions

AQA	C2	✓
OCR B	C5	✓
EDEXCEL	C1, C2	✓
CCEA	C1	✓

> To get a top grade, make sure you can write the symbol equation for this reaction.
>
> $BaCl_2(aq) + Na_2SO_4(aq)$
> $\rightarrow BaSO_4(s) + 2NaCl(aq)$

Some **insoluble** salts can be made from the reaction between two solutions. Barium sulfate is an insoluble salt. It can be made by the reaction between solutions of barium chloride and sodium sulfate.

barium chloride + sodium sulfate → barium sulfate + sodium chloride

Precipitation reactions can be used to remove unwanted ions from solutions. This technique is used to treat drinking water and to treat effluent.

PROGRESS CHECK

1. What is formed when sulfuric acid reacts with sodium hydroxide?
2. What is the reaction between an acid and a base called?
3. Which ions are found in all acids?
4. What sort of salt does nitric acid produce?
5. What is produced when acids react with metal oxides?

5. A salt and water.
4. Nitrates.
3. Hydrogen, H^+ ions.
2. Neutralisation.
1. Sodium Sulfate + Water.

5.3 Limestone

LEARNING SUMMARY

After studying this section, you should be able to:

- Understand the classification of rocks into three types: sedimentary, igneous and metamorphic.
- Recall that limestone is calcium carbonate and explain how it was formed.
- Write an equation for the thermal decomposition of calcium carbonate.
- Write an equation for the reaction between calcium oxide and water.
- Recall the many useful products that are made from limestone.

Types of rock

OCR A	C3	✓
OCR B	C2	✓
EDEXCEL	C1	✓

Rocks can be classified into three groups: **sedimentary**, **metamorphic** and **igneous**.

- **Limestone** and **chalk** are **sedimentary rocks**. These rocks sometimes contain **fossils** and are relatively soft and easy to erode. Sedimentary rocks are formed when layers of sediment are compacted over millions of years. The presence of shell fragments in fossils indicate that the rocks formed in a **marine environment**.
- **Marble** is an example of a **metamorphic rock**. Marble is made when limestone or chalk are subjected to high pressures and temperatures.
- **Granite** is an example of an **igneous rock**. Igneous rocks are harder than metamorphic rocks which, in turn, are harder than sedimentary rocks. They are formed when **magma** (liquid rock below the Earth's surface) or **lava**

(liquid rock above the Earth's surface) cool down and solidify. The faster the crystals in the rocks form the smaller the crystal will be.

Natural geological processes, such as **sedimentation** and **evaporation**, lead to the formation of valuable resources such as salt, limestone and coal.

Limestone

AQA	C1	✓
OCR B	C2	✓
EDEXCEL	C1	✓
WJEC	C3	✓
CCEA	C2	✓

The materials used in everyday life, such as metals, ceramics and polymers, are chemicals or mixtures of chemicals. Some materials, such as cotton, paper, silk and wool, are made from living things.

Raw materials from the Earth's crust can be made into useful new **synthetic materials**. Chemical industries developed in the north-west of England because important resources including salt, limestone and coal could be found nearby.

> **KEY POINT**
>
> When limestone (calcium carbonate) is heated, it breaks down to form **quicklime** (calcium oxide) and carbon dioxide.

calcium carbonate → calcium oxide + carbon dioxide

$$CaCO_3(s) \rightarrow CaO(s) + CO_2(g)$$

This is an example of a **thermal decomposition** reaction.

> **KEY POINT**
>
> Quicklime (calcium oxide) can be reacted with water to form **slaked lime** (calcium hydroxide). A solution of slaked lime is known as **limewater**.

calcium oxide + water → calcium hydroxide

$$CaO(s) + H_2O(l) \rightarrow Ca(OH)_2(s)$$

Calcium carbonate, calcium oxide and calcium hydroxide are all bases and so can be used to neutralise acidic lakes and soils.

Limewater is used to test for the presence of the gas carbon dioxide. Carbon dioxide turns limewater cloudy.

calcium hydroxide + carbon dioxide → calcium carbonate + water

$$Ca(OH)_2(aq) + CO_2(g) \rightarrow CaCO_3(s) + H_2O(l)$$

When limestone is heated, the mass decreases because the gas carbon dioxide is produced.

Limestone quarry

The thermal decomposition of limestone is an example of a reaction that takes in heat. This is called an endothermic reaction. The formula $CaCO_3$ shows us the type and ratio of atoms present. Here, the calcium, carbon and oxygen atoms are present in the ratio 1 : 1 : 3. Calcium oxide is an example of a compound that is held together by **ionic bonds**. Ionic bonding involves the transfer of electrons. This forms ions with opposite charges, which then attract each other.

Uses of limestone

AQA	C1	✓
OCR B	C2	✓
EDEXCEL	C1	✓
WJEC	C3	✓
CCEA	C2	✓

Limestone is used to make iron and steel and to build roads. It can also be used to make a range of building materials.

- **Cement** is produced by roasting powdered clay with powdered limestone in a rotating kiln. If water is added, and the mixture is allowed to set, it forms the hard, stone-like material cement. Clay can also be used to make bricks.
- When water is mixed with cement and sand, and then allowed to set, **mortar** is made.
- **Concrete** is made by mixing cement, sand and aggregate (rock chippings) with water. When water is added to cement it **hydrates** and binds together all the particles to form a material that is as hard as rock. Concrete is tough and cheap; it is widely used in building, for example, bridges.
- **Reinforced concrete** is a useful **composite material**. It is made by setting concrete around steel supports. This material combines the hardness of concrete with the flexibility of steel.
- **Glass** can be made by heating up a mixture of limestone (calcium carbonate), sand (silicon dioxide) and soda (sodium carbonate) until the mixture melts.

PROGRESS CHECK

1. What is the main chemical in limestone?
2. What type of rock is limestone?
3. What type of rock is marble?
4. What type of rock is granite?
5. When calcium carbonate is heated fiercely a chemical reaction takes place.
   a) Write a balanced symbol equation for this reaction.
   b) Why does the sample of calcium carbonate have a lower mass after heating?

b) The gas carbon dioxide is given off, which has mass.
5. a) $CaCO_3(s) \rightarrow CaO(s) + CO_2(g)$
4. Igneous rock.
3. Metamorphic rock.
2. Sedimentary rock.
1. Calcium carbonate.

5.4 Metal carbonate reactions

LEARNING SUMMARY

After studying this section, you should be able to:

- Understand what is happening when a metal carbonate undergoes thermal decomposition.
- Write balanced equations for thermal decomposition reactions of metal carbonates.
- Write balanced equations for metal carbonate reactions with acids.
- Predict the salt produced when a metal carbonate reacts with a given acid.
- Describe the procedure for making a soluble salt from the reaction between a metal carbonate and acid.

Thermal decomposition reactions

AQA	C1	✓
OCR B	C2	✓
EDEXCEL	C1	✓
WJEC	C3	✓
CCEA	C2	✓

When calcium carbonate is heated fiercely it decomposes to form calcium oxide and carbon dioxide. The general equation for the reaction is:

metal carbonate → metal oxide + carbon dioxide

Other metal carbonates, including the carbonates of copper, iron, manganese, calcium, magnesium, and zinc, decompose in a similar way when they are heated. When copper carbonate is heated it breaks down to give copper oxide and carbon dioxide. Copper(II) carbonate is green while copper(II) oxide is black. The colour change shows a new substance has been made.

Heating copper carbonate

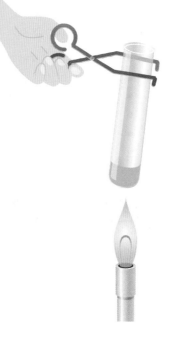

Be able to give the symbol equation for this reaction.
$CuCO_3 \rightarrow CuO + CO_2$

copper(II) carbonate → copper(II) oxide + carbon dioxide

Group 1 carbonates and naming compounds

AQA	C1	✓
EDEXCEL	C1	✓
WJEC	C3	✓
CCEA	C2	✓

Not all metal carbonates of group 1 metals will decompose at the temperatures that can be reached using a Bunsen burner.

If two elements join together in a chemical reaction, the name of the compound is given by the two elements that have joined together, for example:

sodium + chlorine → sodium chloride

Heating baking powder

OCR B	C1	✓

When metal hydrogencarbonate compounds are heated, they undergo thermal decomposition reactions to form metal carbonates, carbon dioxide and water.

The main chemical compound in baking powder is sodium hydrogencarbonate, $NaHCO_3$. When heated fiercely it reacts to form sodium carbonate, carbon dioxide and water. It is the carbon dioxide produced by the reaction that makes cakes rise.

> Be able to recall the equation that sums up this reaction.
> $2NaHCO_3 \rightarrow Na_2CO_3 + CO_2 + H_2O$

sodium hydrogencarbonate → sodium carbonate + carbon dioxide + water

Making salts from metal carbonates

AQA	C2	✓
OCR B	C2	✓
EDEXCEL	C1	✓
WJEC	C1	✓
CCEA	C1, C2	✓

Acids can be neutralised by metal carbonates to form salts. Most metal carbonates are insoluble, so they are bases, but they are not alkalis. When acids are neutralised by metal carbonates, a salt, water and carbon dioxide are produced. This means that rocks, such as limestone, that contain metal carbonate compounds are damaged by acid rain. The general equation for the reaction is:

metal carbonate + acid → salt + water + carbon dioxide

A gas (carbon dioxide) is made so bubbles will be seen. The name of the salt produced depends on the acid and the metal carbonate used.

- Hydrochloric acid makes chloride salts.
- Sulfuric acid makes sulfate salts.
- Nitric acid makes nitrate salts.
- Ethanoic acid is neutralised to form ethanoate salts.
- Phosphoric acid is neutralised to form phosphate salts.

The reactions between acids and metal carbonates are exothermic.

Examples of carbonate reactions

AQA	C2	✓
OCR A	C6	✓
OCR B	C2	✓
EDEXCEL	C1	✓
WJEC	C1	✓
CCEA	C1, C2	✓

zinc carbonate + sulfuric acid → zinc sulfate + water + carbon dioxide

$$ZnCO_3 + H_2SO_4 \rightarrow ZnSO_4 + H_2O + CO_2$$

copper(II) carbonate + hydrochloric acid → copper(II) chloride + water + carbon dioxide

$$CuCO_3 + 2HCl \rightarrow CuCl_2 + H_2O + CO_2$$

Make sure you can apply this idea to other examples.

Making copper chloride

AQA	C2	✓
OCR A	C6	✓
OCR B	C2	✓
EDEXCEL	C1, C3	✓
WJEC	C1	✓
CCEA	C1	✓

The diagram below shows how copper chloride salt is made.

Making copper chloride

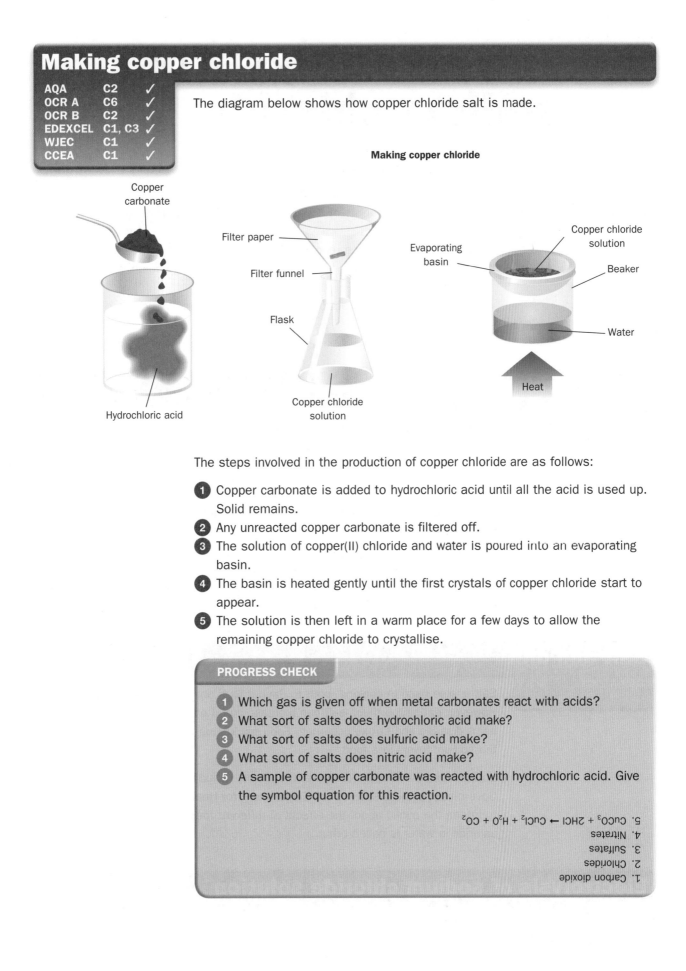

The steps involved in the production of copper chloride are as follows:

1. Copper carbonate is added to hydrochloric acid until all the acid is used up. Solid remains.
2. Any unreacted copper carbonate is filtered off.
3. The solution of copper(II) chloride and water is poured into an evaporating basin.
4. The basin is heated gently until the first crystals of copper chloride start to appear.
5. The solution is then left in a warm place for a few days to allow the remaining copper chloride to crystallise.

PROGRESS CHECK

1. Which gas is given off when metal carbonates react with acids?
2. What sort of salts does hydrochloric acid make?
3. What sort of salts does sulfuric acid make?
4. What sort of salts does nitric acid make?
5. A sample of copper carbonate was reacted with hydrochloric acid. Give the symbol equation for this reaction.

5. $CuCO_3 + 2HCl \rightarrow CuCl_2 + H_2O + CO_2$
4. Nitrates
3. Sulfates
2. Chlorides
1. Carbon dioxide

5.5 The electrolysis of sodium chloride

LEARNING SUMMARY

After studying this section, you should be able to:

- Recall some important uses of sodium chloride.
- Explain the electrolysis of sodium chloride to produce hydrogen, chlorine and sodium hydroxide.
- Write equations for the reactions that occur at the electrodes.
- Recall the main uses of the products of electrolysing sodium chloride solution.
- Understand why the electrolysis of molten sodium chloride has different products.

Sodium chloride

OCR A	C3, C6	✓
OCR B	C2, C6	✓

Sodium chloride (**common salt**) is an important resource. It is an **ionic compound** formed from the **combination** of a group 1 metal (sodium) and a group 7 non-metal (chlorine). Sodium chloride is dissolved in large quantities in **seawater**.

Salt can be obtained by **mining** or from allowing seawater to **evaporate**; the method used depends on how the salt is to be used and how pure it needs to be. **Quarrying** salt can have a dramatic impact on the environment. **Rock salt** (unpurified salt) is often used on icy roads. The salt lowers the freezing point of water from 0°C to about −5°C. Sprinkling rock salt on roads means that any water present will not freeze to form ice unless the temperature is very low.

Salt and diet

OCR A	C3	✓
OCR B	C2, C5	✓

Salt is also used in cooking, both to **flavour** food and as a **preservative**. However, eating too much salt can increase blood pressure and the chance of heart disease and stroke occurring. **Food packaging** may contain information on the sodium levels in a food.

Sodium ions may come from several sources, including sodium chloride salt. Government bodies, such as the Department for Health, produce guidelines to inform the public about the effects of different foods. A solution of sodium chloride in water is called **brine**.

Electrolysis of sodium chloride solution

AQA	C2	✓
OCR A	C3, C5	✓
OCR B	C2,	✓
	C4–C6	✓
EDEXCEL	C1, C3	✓

The **electrolysis** of concentrated sodium chloride solution is an important industrial process and produces three useful products (hydrogen, chlorine and sodium hydroxide). The electrodes are made of inert materials so they do not react with the useful products made during the electrolysis reaction.

- During electrolysis, pairs of hydrogen ions, H^+ ions, are attracted to the negative electrode where they pick up electrons to form hydrogen molecules, H_2.

  Hydrogen ions + Electrons → Hydrogen molecules
  $$2H^+ \qquad + 2e^- \qquad → H_2$$

- Pairs of chloride ions, Cl^- ions, are attracted to the positive electrode where they deposit electrons to form chlorine molecules.

  Chloride ions → Chlorine molecules + Electrons
  $$2Cl^- \qquad → Cl_2 \qquad\qquad + 2e^-$$

- A solution of sodium hydroxide, NaOH is also produced.

Each of these products (hydrogen, chlorine and sodium hydroxide) can be used to make other useful materials. When there is a mixture of ions, such as Cl^- and OH^- and Na^+ and H^+ as in this case, the products that are formed depends on the **reactivity** of the elements involved. Electrolysis can also be used to **electroplate** objects. This can protect surfaces from **corrosion** and make them more attractive. Copper and silver plating are both produced by electrolysis.

In the electrolysis of a concentration of sodium chloride solution:

- Hydrogen ions are **reduced** to hydrogen molecules; the hydrogen ions both gain an electron to form a hydrogen molecule.
- Chloride ions are **oxidised** to chlorine molecules; the two chloride ions both lose an electron to form a chlorine molecule.

> **KEY POINT**
>
> Reduction and oxidation reactions must always occur together, so they are sometimes referred to as **redox** reactions.

Useful products from the electrolysis of sodium chloride solution

AQA	C2	✓
OCR A	C3	✓
OCR B	C2, C6	✓
EDEXCEL	C1, C3	✓

Chlorine is used:

- to make **bleach**
- to sterilise water
- to produce hydrochloric acid
- in the production of PVC.

Hydrogen is used in the manufacture of margarine.

Sodium hydroxide is an alkali used in paper making and in the manufacture of many products including soaps and detergents, and rayon and acetate fibres.

Electrolysis of molten sodium chloride

AQA	C2	✓
OCR A	C4, C5	✓
OCR B	C6	✓
EDEXCEL	C3	✓

Solid sodium chloride does not conduct electricity because the ions cannot move. However, if sodium chloride is heated until it becomes **molten**, the sodium ions and chloride ions can move and electrolysis can occur.

During the electrolysis of molten sodium chloride, the ions move towards the oppositely charged electrodes. Sodium, Na^+, ions (cations) are attracted to the negative electrode (cathode) where they pick up electrons to form sodium, Na atoms.

Sodium ion + Electron → Sodium atom
Na^+ + e^- → Na

Pairs of chloride ions, Cl^-, ions (anions) are attracted to the positive electrode (anode) where they deposit electrons to form chlorine molecules.

Chloride ions → Chlorine molecules + Electrons
$2Cl^-$ → Cl_2 + $2e^-$

Make sure you can apply these ideas to other examples.

PROGRESS CHECK

1. What groups do sodium and chlorine belong to?
2. Where is sodium chloride found?
3. How are **a)** chlorine, **b)** hydrogen and **c)** sodium hydroxide used?
4. Give the symbol equations to show what happens at each of the electrodes during the electrolysis of molten sodium chloride.

1. Groups 1 and 7.
2. In seawater and in underground deposits.
3. a) In bleach, to sterilise water, production of hydrochloric acid and PVC.
   b) In the manufacture of margarine.
   c) In soap, detergents, paper, rayon, acetate.
4. $Na^+ + e^- →$ Na
   $2Cl^- → Cl_2 + 2e^-$

5.6 Titrations

LEARNING SUMMARY

After studying this section, you should be able to:

- Describe the procedure for carrying out a titration.
- Understand why titrations are repeated until concordant results are obtained.
- Explain how titration can be useful in the preparation of salts.
- Follow the method used to turn a titration result (volume) into number of moles delivered.
- Use a titration result to calculate the concentration of a solution of acid or alkali.

Titration reactions

AQA	C3	✓
OCR A	C6	✓
OCR B	C2, C5	✓
EDEXCEL	C3	✓
WJEC	C3	✓
CCEA	C2	✓

In **titration** reactions, acid and alkali solutions are carefully added together. **Alkalis** are **soluble** bases. Titration reactions are really useful because they can be used to work out the **concentration** of one of the solutions used.

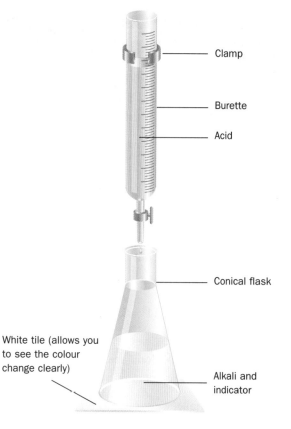

Clamp

Burette

Acid

Conical flask

White tile (allows you to see the colour change clearly)

Alkali and indicator

1. First use a **pipette** to place a known amount of alkali into a flask. Pipettes measure out volumes very accurately. The bottom of the **meniscus** should lie exactly on the mark on the pipette.

2. Place a couple of drops of **indicator** into the flask. Although many types of indicators are available, the two most widely used in titrations are methyl orange (which changes colour from yellow to red) and phenolphthalein (which changes from pink to colourless). Either of these indicators will work well when strong acids, such as hydrochloric acid, nitric acid or sulfuric acid, and strong bases, such as sodium hydroxide or potassium hydroxide, are used. Alternatively, a pH meter can be used to find the end point of the titration. Universal indicator would not be suitable because it is a mixture of several different indicators and it changes colour continuously; a single indicator that changes colour suddenly is much better.

> Phenolphthalein is colourless in acids and pink in alkalis.

3. Place the acid in a **burette**.

4. Add the acid into the flask, a little at a time. Swirl the flask to ensure the solutions are fully mixed. When the indicator changes colour record the volume of acid that has been added. This is a rough titration to work out approximately how much acid to add.

5. Repeat the titration. Using the results from the previous step, it should be possible to know roughly how much acid to use. Add the acid carefully, drop by drop, to find out exactly how much acid is required.

6. Repeat the accurate titrations until you get two **concordant** results (results that are the same).

Although an acid was added to an alkali in the example, it is possible to do the titration the other way round, placing the acid in the flask and the alkali in the burette. A sample of the salt can be obtained by repeating the titration with exactly the same volumes of the reactants but without the indicator. The reaction produces a salt and water. The water can be **evaporated** to leave crystals of the salt. Fertilisers can be made by reacting an acid with an alkali in this way.

Finding the concentration of a solution

AQA	C3	✓
OCR A	C6	✓
OCR B	C5	✓
EDEXCEL	C3	✓
WJEC	C3	✓
CCEA	C2	✓

Example 1: 25 cm^3 of a 0.1 mol dm^{-3} solution of sodium hydroxide was placed in a flask. 22.5 cm^3 of hydrochloric acid was required for **neutralisation**. What is the concentration of the hydrochloric acid?

First, write down the balanced equation for the reaction and the values already known.

NaOH   + HCl →   NaCl + H$_2$O

25 cm^3 22.5 cm^3

0.1 mol dm^{-3} ?

Then work out the number of moles (amount) of sodium hydroxide.

Number of moles = $\dfrac{\text{volume in cm}^3}{1000 \times \text{concentration}}$

$\dfrac{25}{1000} \times 0.1 = 0.0025$ moles

From the balanced equation, 1 mole of sodium hydroxide reacts with 1 mole of hydrochloric acid, so 0.0025 moles of sodium hydroxide reacts with 0.0025 moles of hydrochloric acid.

Finally, work out the concentration of the acid.

Concentration = number of moles × $\dfrac{1000}{\text{volume}}$

       = $0.0025 \times \dfrac{1000}{22.5}$

       = 0.11 mol dm^{-3}

A strong alkali and a weak alkali of the same concentration require the same amount of acid for neutralisation.

Example 2 : 25 cm^3 of sodium hydroxide solution containing 0.1 g of sodium hydroxide pellets was reacted with 0.05 mol dm^{-3} sulfuric acid. What volume of sulfuric acid would be required for neutralisation?

2NaOH + H$_2$SO4 → Na$_2$SO$_4$ + 2H$_2$O

First, work out the number of moles of sodium hydroxide.

Number of moles = $\dfrac{\text{mass of sample}}{\text{formula mass of NaOH}}$

       = $\dfrac{0.1}{40}$

       = 0.0025 moles

From the balanced symbol equation, 2 moles of sodium hydroxide react with 1 mole of sulfuric acid, so 0.0025 moles of sodium hydroxide reacts with 0.00125 moles of sulfuric acid.

Finally, work out the volume of sulfuric acid required.

$$\text{Volume} = \text{number of moles} \times \frac{1000}{\text{concentration}}$$
$$= 0.00125 \times \frac{1000}{0.05}$$
$$= 25 \text{ cm}^3$$

> Try to set out your calculations in a logical order so the examiner can award marks for your working.

PROGRESS CHECK

1. What is the name given to soluble bases?
2. Why is it important to swirl the flask during a titration?
3. What is the colour change for phenolphthalein indicator for alkali to acid?
4. Why is universal indicator unsuitable for finding the end point in a titration reaction?
5. 20.0 cm^3 of a 0.10 mol dm^{-3} solution of sodium hydroxide was placed in a flask. 28.5 cm^3 of hydrochloric acid was required for neutralisation. What is the concentration of the hydrochloric acid?

1. Alkalis.
2. To ensure the solutions are fully mixed.
3. Pink to colourless.
4. Universal indicator would not be suitable because it is a mixture of several different indicators and it changes colour continuously.
5. Moles of sodium hydroxide = 0.002
   Moles of hydrochloric acid = 0.002
   Concentration of acid = $\frac{0.002 \times 1000}{28.5}$
   0.07 mol dm^{-3}.

5.7 Water and solubility

LEARNING SUMMARY

After studying this section, you should be able to:

- Describe how water is purified to make it fit to drink.
- Recall the main ions present in seawater.
- Understand how temperature affects solubility and interpret a 'solubility curve'.
- Describe how washing powders and detergents work.
- Recall that some fabrics require 'dry cleaning' with solvents other than water.

Water

OCR A	C5	✓
OCR B	C4, C6	✓
EDEXCEL	C3	✓
WJEC	C2	✓

The Earth's **hydrosphere** consists of its oceans, seas, lakes and rivers. It consists of water, dissolved salts and gases. Only appropriate sources away from polluted areas are chosen for drinking water. In the UK, water resources are found in lakes, rivers, aquifers (rock formations that contain water) and reservoirs.

Purifying water

AQA	C3	✓
OCR A	C3	✓
OCR B	C4	✓
EDEXCEL	C3	✓
WJEC	C1, C2	✓
CCEA	C2	✓

To purify water, first sedimentation is used to settle impurities. Next, the water is filtered to remove solid impurities. Finally, chlorine is added to the water to kill most of the microorganisms in the water. These tiny organisms could multiply quickly and cause disease, so their numbers must be brought down to acceptable levels.

However, some scientists are concerned that even low levels of chlorine in water could cause health problems when the chlorine reacts with organic substances in the water. Some substances may still remain in the water even after purification. These can sometimes be poisonous so scientists regularly check water quality.

In some areas **fluoride** is added to drinking water. This helps to protect children's teeth from decay. However, some people are concerned about adding chemicals to water and about people's right to choose what is best for themselves and their families.

Water pollution

AQA	C3	✓
OCR B	C4	✓

Nitrate fertilisers can cause problems if they are washed into lakes or streams. Water sources can also be polluted by lead compounds from lead pipes and **pesticides** that have been sprayed near to water resources such as reservoirs.

Formula of salts in seawater

OCR A	C5	✓

As there is no overall charge for the salts in seawater, the charge on the ions can be used to work out the formula of the salt.

Metal ions present in seawater	Non-metal ions present in seawater
Sodium, Na^+	Bromide, Br^-
Potassium, K^+	Chloride, Cl^-
Magnesium, Mg^{2+}	Sulfate, SO_4^{2-}

The compound sodium sulfate contains sodium, Na^+, and sulfate, SO_4^{2-}, ions. For every two sodium ions one sulfate ion is required. The overall formula for the compound is Na_2SO_4.

Solubility

OCR B	C6	✓
EDEXCEL	C2, C3	✓
WJEC	C2	✓
CCEA	C1	✓

Water has many uses including as a coolant, a raw material and as a solvent.

Water is a particularly good **solvent** and dissolves most ionic compounds. The solubility of a substance (called the solute) in water can be measured by measuring the number of grams of the substance that will dissolve in 100 g of water. The more grams of the substance that dissolve the more soluble it is. Generally, the higher the temperature of the water the more soluble a substance will become.

Rules for solubility

| WJEC | C2 | ✓ |
| CCEA | C1 | ✓ |

- All sodium, potassium and ammonium salts are soluble.
- Nitrates are soluble.
- Most chlorides are soluble (apart from silver and lead). Most sulfates are soluble (apart from lead, barium and calcium).
- Solubility curves are used to show how many grams of a particular substance will dissolve in a given solvent. Notice how the solubility of both salts increases as the temperature increases.

Solubility curves

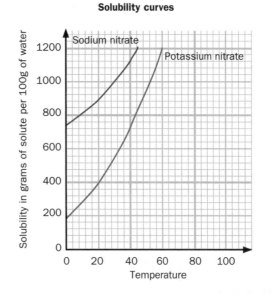

Washing powders and detergents

| OCR B | C6 | ✓ |

Washing powders are used to get clothes clean. They consist of many ingredients including:

- A detergent, to get rid of dirt.
- Water softeners, to remove the hardness from hard water so the detergent can work properly.
- Bleaches, to remove stains.
- Enzymes, to help remove stains at low temperatures.
- Optical brighteners, to make the clothes look very clean.

Clothes labels show symbols that indicate how the item should be washed. Traditionally, washing clothes at lower temperatures than the one shown on the label would save money, but might not get the clothing as clean. More advanced washing powders work to clean clothes even at low temperatures. This helps save energy and money.

Washing powders and washing-up liquids contain chemicals called detergents. Detergent molecules have two parts. Many detergent molecules form a sphere around the grease or fat, which can then be washed off.

Hydrophilic polar head group which forms bonds with water molecules

Hydrophobic tail which avoids water molecules but forms bonds with fat or grease

Dry-cleaning

OCR B	C6	✓

Some fabrics can be damaged by washing them in water and some clothes can be damaged by stains that do not dissolve in water. However, these clothes can be cleaned by dry-cleaning.

> **PROGRESS CHECK**
>
> 1 What is the role of a water softener in a washing powder?
> 2 Why are enzymes added to washing powders?
> 3 Suggest two reasons why some clothes can only be successfully cleaned using the dry-cleaning method.
>
> 1. Water softeners remove hardness from hard water so the detergent can work properly.
> 2. Enzymes are added to help remove stains at low temperatures.
> 3. Some fabrics can be damaged by washing them in water. Other fabrics can be damaged by stains that do not dissolve in water but will dissolve in the solvents used in dry-cleaning.

5.8 Hard and soft water

LEARNING SUMMARY

After studying this section, you should be able to:

- Understand the terms 'hard water' and 'soft water' and the advantages/disadvantages of each.
- Describe a simple test to detect hardness in water.
- Recall that calcium and magnesium salts are responsible for 'hardness' in water.
- Write an equation to show how temporary hardness is removed by boiling water.
- Recognise that ion exchange columns are used to remove all types of hardness from water.

The importance of water

AQA	C3	✓
OCR B	C4, C6	✓
EDEXCEL	C3	✓
WJEC	C2	✓

Water is an extremely important resource. The human body consists of about **70% water** and you lose around two and a half litres of water every day. Most of this planet is covered in water, but the vast majority of this water is unsuitable to drink because it is in oceans and seas.

Hard and soft water

AQA	C3	✓
OCR B	C6	✓
EDEXCEL	C3	✓
WJEC	C2	✓
CCEA	C2	✓

In some parts of the UK tap water is soft. Soft water does not contain dissolved **calcium** or **magnesium salts**. **Distilled water**, or rainwater, can be described as being **soft**. **Tap water** contains dissolved magnesium and calcium salts. This water can be described as being **hard**. As rainwater falls, carbon dioxide in the atmosphere dissolves in the water and then this solution reacts with calcium carbonate to form calcium hydrogencarbonate.

calcium carbonate + water + carbon dioxide → calcium hydrogencarbonate

$$CaCO_3 + H_2O + CO_2 \rightarrow Ca(HCO_3)_2$$

Once the carbonic acid solution reaches the ground it moves through the soils and rocks. If these soils and rocks contain calcium or magnesium compounds, the carbonic acid solution will dissolve the compounds forming hard water.

Forming a lather

AQA	C3	✓
OCR B	C6	✓
EDEXCEL	C3	✓
WJEC	C2	✓
CCEA	C2	✓

> **KEY POINT**
>
> Soft water reacts readily with soap and water to form a lather. When hard water is reacted with soap it forms **scum**.

The calcium (or magnesium) ions react with the **stearate** ions in the soap to form calcium (or magnesium) stearate or scum. If more soap is added, all the calcium and magnesium ions will eventually be removed and only then will lather form.

To find out how hard a sample of water is, add soap solution to a known volume of the sample and shake. The harder the water the more soap solution is required before a good lather is formed. **Soapless detergents**, such as washing-up liquids, are particularly useful because they do not form scum even with hard water.

Types of hard water

AQA	C3	✓
OCR B	C6	✓
EDEXCEL	C3	✓
WJEC	C2	✓
CCEA	C2	✓

> **KEY POINT**
>
> Hard water can be classified as being **permanently hard** or **temporarily hard**. Permanently hard water contains calcium or magnesium chloride and sulfates.

The calcium or magnesium ions remain in the solution even when the water is heated.

To soften permanently hard water, the calcium or magnesium ions need to be removed. One way to do this is to add sodium carbonate. Many washing powders contain this compound, also called washing soda. The sodium carbonate reacts with the calcium or magnesium ions to form precipitates of calcium or magnesium carbonate. As the calcium or magnesium ions have been removed and the water has been softened, the detergent in the washing powder will now work better.

sodium carbonate + calcium chloride → sodium chloride + calcium carbonate

$$Na_2CO_3(aq) + CaCl_2(aq) \rightarrow 2NaCl(aq) + CaCO_3(s)$$

KEY POINT

Temporarily hard water contains calcium or magnesium hydrogencarbonate.

On heating, the hydrogencarbonate ions decompose to form carbonate ions. These ions react with the calcium or magnesium ions present to form precipitates, leaving the water softer.

$$Ca(HCO_3)_2 \rightarrow CaCO_3 + H_2O + CO_2$$

Advantages and disadvantages of different types of water

AQA	C3	✓
OCR B	C6	✓
WJEC	C2	✓
CCEA	C2	✓

Hard water has some health benefits:

- It helps to develop and maintain strong bones and teeth.
- It helps to protect against heart disease.

Soft water also has some advantages:

- Using soft water for cleaning reduces costs because less soap is needed.

KEY POINT

Temporarily hard water can cause **limescale**, which builds up on appliances such as kettles and in central heating systems.

Over time, the amount of limescale increases and the efficiency of the appliance is reduced, so the appliance will cost more to run. Limescale can be removed with **weak acids** such as vinegar. These weak acids react with limescale to give a soluble calcium salt, water and carbon dioxide, but do not react with metals.

Weak acids are better than strong acids at cleaning limescale because they react with the limescale but not with the appliance itself, for example, the kettle.

Ion exchange columns

AQA	C3	✓
OCR B	C6	✓
WJEC	C2	✓
CCEA	C2	✓

Ion exchange columns can also be used to soften hard water. The column contains beads coated in sodium or hydrogen ions. Hard water is passed through the column. The calcium or magnesium ions in the hard water are exchanged for the sodium or hydrogen ions. Some people prefer the taste of soft water or simply want to remove some of the substances dissolved in their tap water to improve its quality. At home, water filters containing carbon, silver or ion exchange resins can all be used to remove some of the dissolved substances present in tap water.

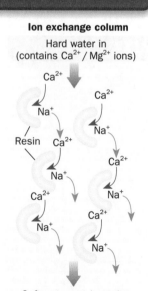

Ion exchange column

Hard water in
(contains Ca^{2+} / Mg^{2+} ions)

Resin

Soft water out (contains
no / very few Ca^{2+} / Mg^{2+} ions)

Desalination of seawater

| AQA | C3 | ✓ |
| WJEC | C2 | ✓ |

Make sure you can draw the apparatus used to distil seawater i.e. a flask connected to a Liebig condenser, which is sloping downwards to a collecting vessel.

Pure water can be produced from seawater by **distillation**, but the process requires a great deal of energy to heat the impure water up to its boiling point. This makes the process too expensive to be worthwhile unless the fuel to be used is very cheap or the pure water is in particular demand.

Seawater contains very high levels of **dissolved salts** that would make you very ill.

PROGRESS CHECK

1. What percentage of a human body is water?
2. Which types of salts make water hard?
3. What is the name of the chemical in washing soda?
4. Which types of ions are involved in an ion exchange column?
5. Explain how you could identify whether a sample of water was soft, permanently hard or temporarily hard.

1. About 70%.
2. Magnesium and calcium salts.
3. Sodium carbonate.
4. Calcium or magnesium ions are exchanged for sodium or hydrogen ions.
5. The soft water would form a lather quickly with just a little soap solution.
If the temporarily hard water sample was boiled and then allowed to cool, the hydrogencarbonate ions in the sample would decompose to form carbonate ions. These ions would react with the calcium or magnesium ions present to form precipitates, leaving the water softer. This sample would now react readily to form lather.
Boiling would not affect the permanently hard water, which would react with the soap solution to form scum.

Sample GCSE questions

1   Many households have a water-softener, which works by ion exchange.

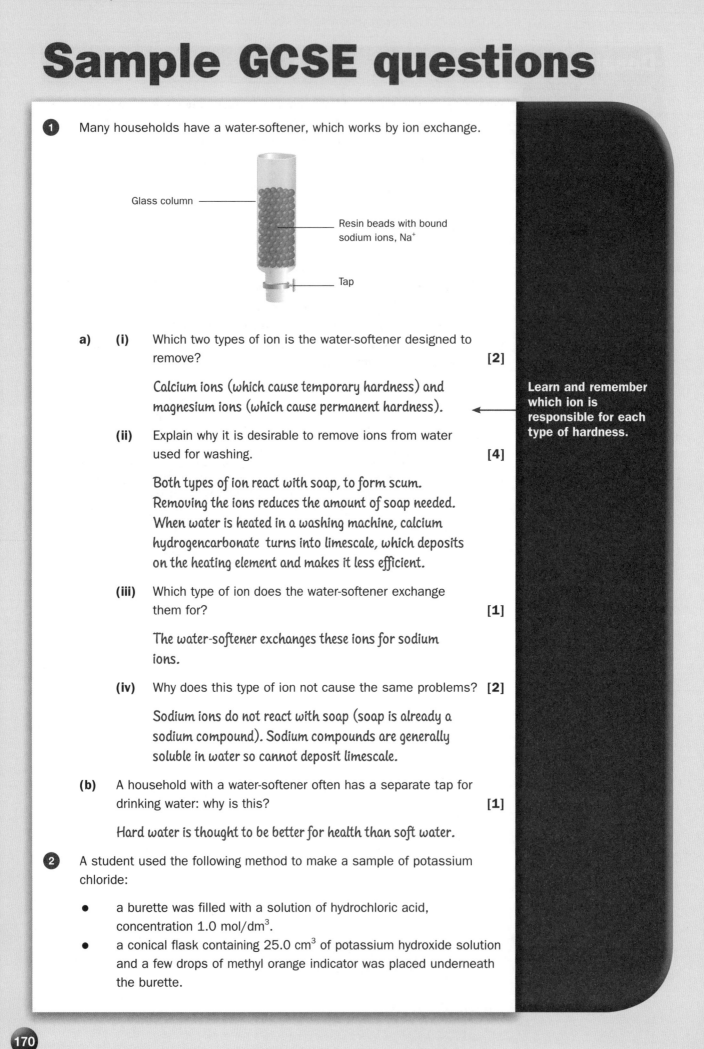

Glass column

Resin beads with bound
sodium ions, Na⁺

Tap

a)   **(i)**   Which two types of ion is the water-softener designed to
remove?   **[2]**

*Calcium ions (which cause temporary hardness) and
magnesium ions (which cause permanent hardness).*

Learn and remember
which ion is
responsible for each
type of hardness.

(ii)   Explain why it is desirable to remove ions from water
used for washing.   **[4]**

*Both types of ion react with soap, to form scum.
Removing the ions reduces the amount of soap needed.
When water is heated in a washing machine, calcium
hydrogencarbonate turns into limescale, which deposits
on the heating element and makes it less efficient.*

(iii)   Which type of ion does the water-softener exchange
them for?   **[1]**

*The water-softener exchanges these ions for sodium
ions.*

(iv)   Why does this type of ion not cause the same problems?   **[2]**

*Sodium ions do not react with soap (soap is already a
sodium compound). Sodium compounds are generally
soluble in water so cannot deposit limescale.*

(b)   A household with a water-softener often has a separate tap for
drinking water: why is this?   **[1]**

Hard water is thought to be better for health than soft water.

2   A student used the following method to make a sample of potassium
chloride:

*   a burette was filled with a solution of hydrochloric acid,
concentration 1.0 mol/dm³.
*   a conical flask containing 25.0 cm³ of potassium hydroxide solution
and a few drops of methyl orange indicator was placed underneath
the burette.

Sample GCSE questions

- The acid was run from the burette into the flask, until the indicator just changed colour. The volume of acid delivered was noted.
- The experiment was repeated, without the indicator, but adding exactly the same volume of the acid as before.
- The resulting solution was left to crystallise in a warm place.

(a) **(i)** Write a balanced equation for the reaction between hydrochloric acid and potassium hydroxide. **[2]**

$$HCl(aq) + KOH(aq) \rightarrow KCl(aq) + H_2O(l)$$

> Remember that sodium and potassium hydroxides react in a 1:1 ratio with hydrochloric acid, and these are the most common combinations in titration experiments.

(ii) Why did the student use an indicator the first time, but not the second time? **[2]**

The first time, the indicator showed the volume of acid needed to produce a neutral solution. The second time, the indicator was left out, so as not to contaminate the product.

(b) **(i)** What would be the most accurate way of measuring 25.0 cm^3 of potassium hydroxide into the flask? **[1]**

A pipette is preferred, as it much more accurate than a measuring cylinder.

(ii) If the volume of acid used was 20.0 cm^3, what was the concentration of the potassium hydroxide solution that was being used? **[3]**

$$moles = \frac{volume}{concentration} \times 1000$$

> State which formula you are using; show all working; remember to write the units.

$$moles\ of\ acid = \frac{20.0 \times 1.0}{1000} = 0.02\ mol$$

1:1 ratio in equation, so 0.02 moles alkali are present

$$concentration = \frac{number\ of\ moles \times 1000}{volume}$$

$$= \frac{0.02 \times 1000}{25.0} = 0.8\ mol/dm^3$$

(ii) Explain why leaving the resulting solution in a warm place caused crystals to form. **[2]**

The warmth helped the water to evaporate. The solution became saturated and the potassium chloride was deposited as crystals.

> When asked to 'explain', always give as much detail as you can fit in.

Exam practice questions

1 Hydrochloric acid is a strong acid and ethanoic acid is a weak acid.

   (a) State which acid is fully ionised when in solution. .... **[1]**

   (b) State which ion is produced by both acids when in solution. .... **[1]**

   (c) Which acid would react more rapidly with magnesium ribbon if the concentration was the same? **[1]**

   ....

   (d) Explain why ethanoic acid is better than hydrochloric acid for descaling a kettle. **[2]**

   ....

   ....

2 Sulfuric acid reacts with magnesium metal, giving off a gas.

   (a) Which gas is produced in this reaction? .... **[1]**

   (b) How does the pH of the acid change as it reacts? .... **[1]**

   (c) What compound is produced in this reaction? .... **[1]**

   (d) Give the names of two other substances that would react with sulfuric acid to produce the same compound. **[2]**

   ....

3 Limestone is an important raw material that is quarried in many parts of the UK.

   (a) What is the name of the main chemical present in limestone? **[1]**

   ....

   (b) Describe how limestone is turned into cement. **[2]**

   ....

   ....

   (c) Describe four factors that should be taken into consideration when quarrying for limestone. Your answer must include at least one each of the environmental, economic and social effects. **[4]**

   ....

   ....

   ....

   ....

4 To prepare a sample of copper(II) sulfate, sulfuric acid can be reacted with copper(II) carbonate. To make sure all of the acid has been neutralised, an excess of copper(II) carbonate is used.

   (a) By what process would any unreacted copper(II) carbonate be removed? **[1]**

   ....

Exam practice questions

(b) The copper(II) sulfate produced is a blue solution. How might a solid be obtained? **[1]**

....

(c) Write a word equation for the reaction that takes place. **[2]**

....

(d) Explain why the acid becomes warm as it reacts. **[1]**

....

5 In the 'Chlor-alkali' industry, a solution called 'brine' is electrolysed to make useful products.

(a) What chemical is dissolved in the brine solution? **[1]**

....

(b) In the electrolysis, two gases are produced. What are they? **[2]**

....

....

(c) What is the alkali that gives the industry its name? .... **[1]**

(d) Explain why the electrodes must be chemically inert. **[1]**

....

6 The concentration of a sodium hydroxide solution can be established by titrating it with a solution of hydrochloric acid, of known concentration.

(a) Which solution would be placed in the flask? **[1]**

....

(b) What else should be added to the flask, before the titration starts? **[1]**

....

(c) What piece of apparatus allows us to measure the volume of solution needed for neutralisation? **[1]**

....

(d) 25 cm^3 of the sodium hydroxide solution was neutralised by 50 cm^3 of 0.1 mol/dm^3 hydrochloric acid. Calculate the concentration of the sodium hydroxide. **[2]**

....

....

7 High levels of nitrates in drinking water have been linked to 'blue baby' syndrome in infants.

(a) Explain how nitrates get into drinking water. **[2]**

....

....

Exam practice questions

(b) Why is it not possible to remove nitrates by filtration? **[1]**

....

(c) Explain why chlorine is added to drinking water. **[1]**

....

(d) Describe how nitrate levels in drinking water can be reduced. **[1]**

....

8 Tap water varies from region to region in the UK. Some regions have soft water, some have temporary hard water and some have permanent hard water.

(a) What is the chemical that causes temporary hardness in water? **[1]**

....

(b) Describe two problems that arise from temporary hardness in water. **[2]**

....

....

(c) Explain why more soap is needed in hard water **[3]**

....

....

(d) Describe how an ion-exchanger removes hardness. **[1]**

....

9 Acids and alkalis are chemical opposites, in that the one neutralises the other, and vice versa.

(a) What is the formula of the ion present in acid solutions? .... **[1]**

(b) What is the formula of the ion present in alkaline solutions? .... **[1]**

(c) Write a balanced ionic equation for the reaction between these two ions. **[2]**

....

(d) Describe what happens to the pH of an acid, when a solution of alkali is gradually added. **[1]**

....

10 Marble is a metamorphic rock, formed from limestone, under conditions of high pressure and temperature. Both types of rock are mostly calcium carbonate.

(a) How is marble different from limestone in its properties? **[1]**

....

(b) Marble undergoes thermal decomposition, like limestone. What are the products of the thermal decomposition of marble? **[2]**

....

Exam practice questions

(c) Which solution is used to test for carbon dioxide gas? **[1]**

....

11 Baking powder is added to cake mixes to make the cakes rise when they are baked.

(a) What is the main chemical present in baking powder? **[1]**

....

(b) What type of reaction happens to baking powder at high temperature? **[1]**

....

(c) Explain how baking powder makes the cake rise. **[2]**

....

....

(d) Balance the following equation:

....$NaHCO_3$(s) → ....Na_2CO_3(s) + ...CO_2(g) + ...H_2O(l) **[1]**

12 Indicators are a group of chemicals that turn one colour in acid and a different colour in alkali.

(a) Describe what an indicator is needed for in a titration experiment. **[2]**

....

....

(b) Methyl orange is red in acid. What colour does it become in alkali? **[1]**

....

(c) Explain why Universal (full-range) indicator is not used in titrations. **[1]**

....

13 Although most of the Earth's surface is covered by water, there are still serious water shortages in many areas of the World. Seawater contains high concentrations of salts, which make it unsuitable for drinking or for watering crops.

Explain why it is too costly to remove the salts from seawater, on a large scale, to turn it into fresh water for drinking and for watering crops.

The quality of written communication will be assessed in your answer to this question. **[6]**

....

....

....

....

....

....

Calculation and physical chemistry

The following topics are covered in this chapter:

- Relative formula mass and percentage composition
- Calculating masses
- Calculations
- Rates of reaction
- Reversible reactions
- The Haber process
- Exothermic and endothermic reactions
- Explaining energy changes

6.1 Relative formula mass and percentage composition

LEARNING SUMMARY

After studying this section, you should be able to:

- Recognise the atomic number and the mass number for an element on the periodic table.
- Work out the relative formula mass of a compound from the mass numbers of its elements.
- Calculate the number of moles of an element in a given mass.
- Calculate the number of moles of a compound in a given mass.
- Calculate the percentage by mass of one element in a compound.

Why relative atomic mass is used

AQA	C2	✓
OCR A	C5, C6	✓
OCR B	C3, C5	✓
EDEXCEL	C2	✓
WJEC	C2, C3	✓
CCEA	C1	✓

The **relative atomic mass (RAM** or **A_r)** is used to compare the masses of different atoms.

KEY POINT

The relative atomic mass of an element is the average mass of one atom of its **isotopes** compared with an atom of carbon-12.

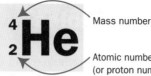

Mass number

Atomic number
(or proton number)

Relative formula mass

AQA	C2	✓
OCR A	C5, C6	✓
OCR B	C3, C5	✓
EDEXCEL	C2	✓
WJEC	C2, C3	✓
CCEA	C1	✓

KEY POINT

The **relative formula mass (RFM** or M_r) of a substance is worked out by adding together the relative atomic masses of all the atoms in the ratio indicated by the formula.

Example: For nitrogen, N_2:

$$N_2$$

$(2 \times 14) = 28$

The relative formula mass of N_2 is 28. Nitrogen molecules contain a triple covalent bond, which is very strong. This makes nitrogen molecules very stable.

Example: For carbon dioxide, CO_2:

$$CO_2$$

$12 + (2 \times 16) = 44$

The relative formula mass of CO_2 is 44.

Example: For water, H_2O:

$$H_2O$$

$(2 \times 1) + 16 = 18$

The relative formula mass of H_2O is 18.

Moles

AQA	C2	✓
OCR B	C5	✓
EDEXCEL	C3	✓
WJEC	C3	✓
CCEA	C1	✓

The relative formula mass of a substance in grams is known as **1 mole** of the substance. This is also known as the molar mass. The units for molar mass are **g/mol**. 1 mole of CO_2 is 44 g and 1 mole of H_2O is 18 g. The number of moles of a substance present can be calculated using the formula below.

$$\text{Number of moles} = \frac{\text{mass of sample}}{\text{relative formula mass of the substance}}$$

Calculations using moles

AQA	C2	✓
OCR B	C3, C5	✓
EDEXCEL	C3	✓
WJEC	C2, C3	✓
CCEA	C1, C2	✓

The relative formula mass of water is 18 so the molar mass is 18 g.

$$\text{Number of moles} = \frac{9}{18} = 0.5$$

There are 0.5 moles in 9 g of water.

Example: What is the mass of 0.5 moles of nitrogen?

The relative formula mass of nitrogen is 28.

$$\frac{\text{Mass of}}{\text{sample}} = \frac{\text{number}}{\text{of moles}} \times \frac{\text{relative formula}}{\text{mass of the substance}} = 0.5 \times 28 = 14 \text{ g}$$

The mass of 0.5 moles of nitrogen is 14 g.

Compounds consist of atoms of two or more different elements that have been chemically joined together. The percentage composition of an element in the compound can be calculated using the formula below.

$$\textbf{Percentage mass of an element in a compound} = \frac{\textbf{relative atomic mass} \times \textbf{no. of atoms}}{\textbf{relative formula mass}} \times \textbf{100\%}$$

Example: Ammonium nitrate is used as a fertiliser. Plants absorb fertiliser through their roots, so fertilisers must be soluble. Find the percentage composition of nitrogen in this compound.

- RAM of N = 14
- RAM of H = 1
- RAM of O = 16
- RAM of S = 32

The formula mass of ammonium nitrate, NH_4NO_3 is:

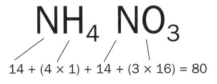

$$NH_4 \; NO_3$$
$$14 + (4 \times 1) + 14 + (3 \times 16) = 80$$

The percentage of nitrogen in ammonium nitrate is 35%,

since $\dfrac{2 \times 14}{80} \times 100\% = 35\%$

Example: Ammonium sulfate is also used as a fertiliser. Find the percentage of nitrogen in this compound.

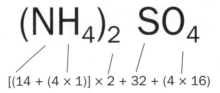

$$(NH_4)_2 \; SO_4$$
$$[(14 + (4 \times 1)] \times 2 + 32 + (4 \times 16)$$

The percentage of nitrogen in ammonium sulfate is 21.2%,

since $\dfrac{2 \times 14}{132} \times 100\% = 21.2\%$

PROGRESS CHECK

1. Why is relative atomic mass used in science?
2. How is the relative formula mass of a substance calculated?
3. What is the relative formula mass of a substance in grams known as?
4. What is the mass of 1 mole of H_2O?
5. a) Find the relative formula mass of a nitrogen molecule, N_2.
   b) Find the relative formula mass of carbon dioxide, CO_2.

1. It is used to compare the masses of different atoms.
2. By adding together the relative atomic masses of all the atoms in the ratio indicated by the formula.
3. Molar mass.
4. 18 g.
5. a) 28 g.
   b) 44 g.

6.2 Calculating masses

LEARNING SUMMARY

After studying this section, you should be able to:

- Calculate the number of moles in a given mass of a substance.
- Calculate the mass in grams, of a given number of moles of a substance.
- Use a balanced equation to relate the number of moles of one substance to the number of moles of another.
- Understand how percentage yield is calculated.
- Understand the term 'atom economy' and know how to calculate it for a given reaction.

Calculating the mass of products

AQA	C2	✓
OCR A	C6	✓
OCR B	C3, C5	✓
EDEXCEL	C2	✓
WJEC	C2	✓
CCEA	C1, C2	✓

The masses of **products** and **reactants** can be worked out using the **balanced equation** for the reaction.

Example: What mass of water is produced when 8 g of hydrogen is burned? Relative atomic mass:

H = 1, O = 16

First, write down what happens during the reaction as a word equation.

hydrogen + oxygen → water

Then write it as a balanced symbol equation.

$2H_2 + O_2 \rightarrow 2H_2O$

Next, calculate the **relative formula mass** of a hydrogen molecule and a water molecule.

The relative formula mass of hydrogen, H_2:

$$H_2$$

$$2 \times 1 = 2$$

The relative formula mass of water, H_2O:

$$H_2O$$

$$(2 \times 1) + 16 = 18$$

It is now possible to calculate the number of moles in 8 g of hydrogen.

$$\frac{8}{2} = 4 \text{ moles}$$

Next, examine the balanced symbol equation. Every 2 moles of hydrogen makes 2 moles of water. This means 4 moles of hydrogen will produce 4 moles of water.

Finally, work out the mass of 4 moles of water by rearranging the moles equation.

$$\text{Mass of sample} = \text{number of moles} \times \text{relative formula mass}$$
$$= 4 \times 18$$
$$= 72$$

This shows that if 8 g of hydrogen is burned completely, 72 g of water vapour will be produced.

Calculating the mass of reactants

AQA	C2	✓
OCR A	C6	✓
OCR B	C3, C5	✓
EDEXCEL	C2	✓
WJEC	C2	✓
CCEA	C1, C2	✓

The equation for a reaction can also be used to calculate how much of the reactants should be used to produce a given amount of the product.

Example: What mass of magnesium should be used to produce 60 g of magnesium oxide?

Relative atomic mass:

Mg = 24   O = 16

First, write down what happens during the reaction as a word equation.

magnesium + oxygen → magnesium oxide

Then write it as a balanced symbol equation.

$2Mg + O_2 \rightarrow 2MgO$

Next, calculate the relative formula mass of magnesium oxide.

The relative formula mass of magnesium oxide, MgO:

$$MgO$$

$$24 + 16 = 40$$

The relative atomic mass of magnesium is given as 24. It is now possible to calculate the number of moles in 60 g of magnesium oxide.

$$\frac{60}{40} = 1.5 \text{ moles}$$

Next, examine the balanced symbol equation. To make 2 moles of magnesium oxide, 2 moles of magnesium are needed. So, to make 1.5 moles of magnesium oxide, 1.5 moles of magnesium are needed.

Finally, work out the mass of 1.5 moles of magnesium oxide by rearranging the moles equation.

Mass of sample = number of moles × relative formula mass
$$= 1.5 \times 24$$
$$= 36$$

This shows that to make 60 g of magnesium oxide, 36 g of magnesium should be burned.

Percentage yield

AQA	C2	✓
OCR A	C6	✓
OCR B	C3, C5	✓
EDEXCEL	C2	✓
WJEC	C2	✓
CCEA	C1	✓

The amount of product made in a reaction is called the **yield**. Although atoms are never gained or lost during a chemical reaction, the yield of a reaction is often less than the yield predicted. This can be for a number of reasons:

- The reaction is **reversible** and does not go to completion.
- Some of the product is lost during **filtering**, **evaporation**, when transferring liquids or during **heating**.
- There may be **side-reactions** occurring that produce other products.

The amount of product actually made compared with the maximum calculated yield is called the **percentage yield**. A 100% yield means no product has been lost; a 0% yield means no product has been made.

> **KEY POINT**
>
> $$\text{Percentage yield} = \frac{\text{mass of product}}{\text{maximum calculated yield}} \times 100\%$$

Scientists try to choose reactions with either a high percentage yield or **high atom economy**. This contributes towards **sustainable development** by reducing waste. A 100% atom economy means that all the reactant atoms have been made into the desired products.

Making ethanol

AQA	C1	✓
OCR B	C3, C6	✓
EDEXCEL	C3	✓
CCEA	C2	✓

Ethanol can be made by two different methods. These different methods have very different atom economies. When ethanol is made by reacting ethene with steam, the process has an atom economy of 100%.

$$C_2H_4 + H_2O \rightarrow C_2H_5OH$$

When ethanol is made by fermentation, the atom economy is less.

$$C_6H_{12}O_6 \rightarrow 2C_2H_5OH + 2CO_2$$

$$\text{Atom economy} = \frac{M_r \text{ of desired products}}{M_r \text{ of all products}} \times 100\%$$

$$= \frac{92}{180} = 51.1\%$$

Waste products are undesirable as they cannot always be sold for profit, their disposal can be costly and cause environmental and social problems.

PROGRESS CHECK

1 What mass of water vapour is produced when 4 g of hydrogen is burned?
2 What mass of water vapour is produced when 16 g of hydrogen is burned?
3 Consider the equation below.
$CaCO_3 \rightarrow CaO + CO_2$
If 5.0 g is heated fiercely, what mass of calcium oxide is produced?

3. 2.8 g.
2. 144 g.
1. 36 g.

6.3 Calculations

LEARNING SUMMARY

After studying this section, you should be able to:

- Work out the empirical formula of a compound from the masses of elements present.
- Recall that the number of particles in a mole of substance is Avogadro's number.
- Calculate the number of moles present in a given volume of a gas.
- Calculate the number of moles present in a given volume of a solution of known concentration.
- Calculate the concentration of a solution where a given number of moles of solute is dissolved in a given volume of solution.

Finding the empirical formula

AQA	C2	✓
OCR B	C5	✓
EDEXCEL	C2	✓
CCEA	C1	✓

KEY POINT

The **empirical formula** of a compound is the ratio of each kind of atom in its simplest form.

Example: Find the empirical formula of magnesium oxide formed when 12 g of magnesium reacts with 8 g of oxygen atoms. Deal with the magnesium and oxygen separately.

Practise writing out this calculation until you can remember all the steps involved.

	Mg	O
State the number of grams that combine.	12	8
Change the grams to moles (divide by A_r).	$\frac{1}{2}$	$\frac{1}{2}$
This is the ratio in which the atoms combine.	0.5	0.5
Get the ratio into its simplest form.	1	1

The simplest ratio of magnesium atoms to oxygen atoms is 1 : 1 so the empirical formula is MgO.

Molar mass

OCR B	C5	✓
EDEXCEL	C3	✓
WJEC	C3	✓

The **molar mass** is the mass of 1 mole of a substance in grams.

The number of moles in a sample of a substance = $\dfrac{\text{mass of sample}}{\text{molar mass}}$

Example: How many moles are present in 60 g of calcium carbonate, $CaCO_3$?

The molar mass of calcium carbonate:

$$\underset{40}{\text{Ca}} \quad \underset{12}{\text{C}} \quad \underset{(16 \times 3) = 100}{\text{O}_3}$$

The number of moles in a sample of a substance

$$= \frac{\text{mass of sample}}{\text{molar mass}} = \frac{60 \text{ g}}{100 \text{ g}} = 0.6 \text{ moles}$$

Avogadro's number

| EDEXCEL | C3 | ✓ |
| WJEC | C3 | ✓ |

One mole of any substance contains 6×10^{23} particles. This is known as **Avogadro's number**. It can be used to work out how many moles of a substance are present.

Number of moles = $\dfrac{\text{number of particles in the sample}}{\text{number of particles in one mole}}$

Example: A sample contains 4.5×10^{23} particles. How many moles are there in this sample?

$$\text{Number of moles} = \frac{\text{number of particles in the sample}}{\text{number of particles in one mole}} = \frac{4.5 \times 10^{23}}{6 \times 10^{23}}$$

$$= 0.75 \text{ moles}$$

Gas volumes

| OCR B | C5 | ✓ |
| EDEXCEL | C3 | ✓ |

One mole of any gas takes up a volume of **24 dm³** at room temperature and pressure.

Volume in dm³ = number of moles × 24

Example: What is the volume of 1.5 moles of carbon dioxide, CO_2?

Volume in dm³ = number of moles × 24 = 1.5 × 24 = 36 dm³

Example: A sample of gas at room temperature and pressure occupies 40 dm³. How many moles of gas are present?

$$\text{Number of moles} = \frac{\text{volume in dm}^3}{24} = \frac{40}{24} = 1.67 \text{ moles}$$

Concentrations

OCR A	C7	✓
OCR B	C5	✓
EDEXCEL	C3	✓
WJEC	C3	✓
CCEA	C1, C2	✓

The **concentration** of a solution is a measure of how much **solute** is dissolved in 1 dm³ of solution. It is sometimes used to describe how many moles are dissolved in 1 dm³ of solution and has the units **mol dm⁻³**.

$$\text{Concentration} = \frac{\text{moles}}{\text{volume in dm}^3}$$

Example: If 2 moles of sodium hydroxide pellets are added to distilled water and the total volume of solution is 2 dm^3, what is the concentration of the solution?

$$\text{Concentration} = \frac{\text{moles}}{\text{volume in dm}^3} = \frac{2 \text{ moles}}{2 \text{ dm}^3} = 1 \text{ mol dm}^{-3}$$

> Concentration is sometimes used to describe how many grams of a solute are dissolved in 1 dm^3 of solution and has the units g/dm^3 or g dm^{-3}.

It is often very useful to **dilute** concentrated solution such as medicines, baby milk and orange cordial drinks. To dilute a 1.0 mol dm^{-3} solution to a 0.1 mol dm^{-3} solution, take 10 cm^3 of the original solution and place it into a clean flask. Then make it up to 100 cm^3 with distilled water.

PROGRESS CHECK

1. A sample of magnesium contains 3×10^{23} atoms. How many moles of magnesium are in this sample?
2. A sample of iron contains 6×10^{23} atoms. How many moles of iron are in this sample?
3. How many atoms are in 0.1 moles of argon?
4. How many atoms are there in 0.5 moles of sodium?
5. What volume does 12 moles of carbon dioxide occupy?
6. A 750 cm^3 sample of sodium hydroxide solution contains 3 g of solid sodium hydroxide. What is the concentration of this solution in g dm^3?

1. 0.5 moles.
2. 0 moles.
3. 6×10^{22} atoms.
4. 3×10^{23} atoms.
5. 288 dm^3.
6. 4 g dm^3.

6.4 Rates of reaction

LEARNING SUMMARY

After studying this section, you should be able to:

- Describe what is meant by the rate of reaction and how it can be measured.
- Understand the effect of changing the temperature on the rate of a reaction.
- Understand the effect of increasing the surface area on the rate of a reaction.
- Understand the effect of changing concentrations on the rate of a reaction.
- Recall that a catalyst increases the rate of reaction without being used up.

Slow and fast reactions

AQA	C2	✓
OCR A	C6	✓
OCR B	C3, C5	✓
EDEXCEL	C2	✓
CCEA	C2	✓

The **rate of reaction** is equal to either:

- the amount of reactant used up divided by the time taken, or
- the amount of product made divided by the time taken.

Rusting is an example of a reaction that happens very slowly, while **combustion** reactions and explosions happen very quickly. **Explosions** produce a large volume of **gaseous products**. Factories that produce fine powders, such as custard powder, have to be very careful to prevent explosions from occurring.

Measuring rates of reaction

AQA	C2	✓
OCR A	C6	✓
OCR B	C3, C5	✓
EDEXCEL	C2	✓
WJEC	C2	✓
CCEA	C2	✓

The method chosen to follow the rate for a particular reaction depends on the reactants and products involved. When sodium thiosulfate reacts with hydrochloric acid, one of the products is a precipitate of sulfur. The rate of reaction can be followed using a light sensor and a data logger to measure how quickly sulfur is being made. A chemical reaction can only occur if the reacting particles collide with enough energy to react. This is called the **activation energy**. If the particles collide but do not have the minimum energy to react, the particles just bounce apart without reacting.

Measuring the rate of reaction

Gas syringe

Dilute
hydrochloric acid

Magnesium

The rate of a chemical reaction can be measured by:

● How fast the products are being made.
● How fast the reactants are being used up.

The graph below shows the amount of product made in two experiments. The lines are steepest at the start of the reaction in both experiments. The lines start to level out as the reactants get used up. When the line becomes horizontal the reaction has finished. The graph shows that experiment 2 has a faster rate of reaction than experiment 1. However, both experiments produce the same amount of product.

**A graph to show how quickly a product is
made in a chemical reaction**

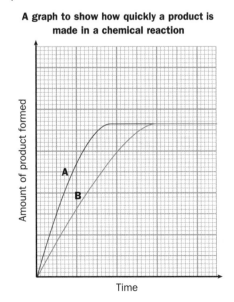

Amount of product formed

A

B

Time

When analysing graphs, the reaction is over when the graph levels out. Reactions stop when one of the reactants is all used up; this reactant is called the **limiting reactant**. The other reactants may not be completely used up and are said to be in **excess**. The amount of product made depends on the amount of reactant used up; the amount of product made is directly proportional to the amount of reactant used. The rate of reaction is measured using units of g/s or g/min or cm^3/s or cm^3/min.

Temperature

If the temperature is increased, the reactant particles move more quickly.

> **KEY POINT**
>
> Increasing the temperature increases the rate of reaction because:
>
> - The particles collide more often.
> - When the particles collide, the collisions have more energy.

Increasing the surface area

> **KEY POINT**
>
> For a reaction to occur, the particles have to **collide**. The greater the surface area the more chance of the reactant particles colliding and the faster the rate of reaction.

With a small surface area (large pieces) the rate of reaction is slow. The particles collide less often. With a large surface area (small pieces) the rate of reaction is higher. The particles collide more often.

Remember, small pieces have a large surface area. The dust caused by fine powders, such as custard powder or flour, can burn explosively because of the large surface area of its particles.

Catalysts

A **catalyst** increases the rate of reaction, but is not itself used up during the reaction. Only a small amount of catalyst is needed to catalyse a large amount of reactants. Catalysts are specific to certain reactions. Catalysts offer an alternative reaction pathway with a **lower activation energy**.

Remember, catalysts do not get used up in reactions. Reactions stop when one of the reactants is all used up.

Concentration and pressure

For a reaction to take place, the reactant particles have to collide. If the concentration is increased there are more reactant particles in the solution. Increasing the concentration increases the rate of reaction because the particles collide more often.

For gases, increasing the pressure has the same effect as increasing the concentration of dissolved particles in solutions. At low concentration the rate of reaction slows down because the particles collide less often. At higher concentration the rate of reaction speeds up because the particles collide more often.

PROGRESS CHECK

1. What happens to the rate of reaction if the concentration of reactants is increased?
2. What happens to the rate of reaction if the pressure of gaseous reactants is increased?
3. How does a catalyst affect the rate of reaction?
4. Explain two ways in which increasing the temperature increases the rate of a chemical reaction.

4. If the temperature is increased the particles move more quickly. This means the particles collide more often and, when they do collide, the collisions have more energy. As more collisions have a level of energy greater than the activation energy, the particles react more quickly.

3. A catalyst increases the rate of reaction without being used up itself.

2. It increases.

1. It increases.

6.5 Reversible reactions

LEARNING SUMMARY

After studying this section, you should be able to:

- Recognise that the symbol $\rightleftharpoons$ shows a reaction is reversible.
- Understand that a reaction that is exothermic in one direction is endothermic in the other direction.
- Explain what is meant by the term 'dynamic equilibrium'.
- Understand the effect of changing conditions on a system at equilibrium.
- Recall that cost, yield and rate of reaction are important in choosing the optimum conditions.

Simple reversible reactions

AQA	C2	✓
OCR A	C7	✓
OCR B	C2, C5	✓
EDEXCEL	C3	✓
WJEC	C3	✓
CCEA	C2	✓

In science, not all reactions go to completion.

KEY POINT

Many chemical reactions are **reversible**; they can proceed both forwards and backwards.

If A and B are reactants and C and D are products, a reversible reaction can be summed up as:

A + B $\rightleftharpoons$ C + D

The two reactants, A and B, can react to make the products C and D; at the same time, C and D can react together to produce A and B.

Exothermic and endothermic reactions

AQA	C2, C3	✓
OCR A	C7	✓
OCR B	C3, C5	✓
EDEXCEL	C3	✓
CCEA	C2	✓

If the forwards reaction is **exothermic** (gives out energy), then the backwards reaction is **endothermic** (takes in energy). The amount of energy given out by the forwards reaction must be the same as the amount of energy taken in by the backwards reaction.

Example: copper(II) sulfate reactions

First, the **hydrated** (with water) copper sulfate is heated to make **anhydrous** (without water) copper sulfate. Then water is added to the anhydrous copper sulfate to produce hydrated copper sulfate.

Copper(II) sulfate reactions

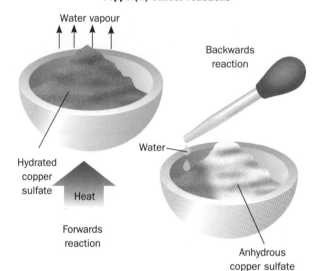

In the forwards reaction, the hydrated copper sulfate takes in energy as it is heated. This is an endothermic reaction.

hydrated copper(II) sulfate (blue) → anhydrous copper(II) sulfate (white) + water

In the backwards reaction, energy is given out when water is added to the anhydrous copper sulfate. This is an exothermic reaction.

anhydrous copper(II) sulfate (white) + water → hydrated copper(II) sulfate (blue)

Dynamic equilibrium

AQA	C3	✓
OCR A	C7	✓
OCR B	C5	✓
EDEXCEL	C3	✓
CCEA	C2	✓

If a reversible reaction takes place inside a closed system (where nothing can enter or leave), an **equilibrium** will eventually be reached. It is a **dynamic equilibrium**: both the forwards and the backwards reactions are taking place at exactly the same rate.

The conditions will affect the position of equilibrium, that is, how much reactant and product are present at equilibrium. If the forwards reaction is exothermic then increasing the temperature will decrease the amount of product made. If the forwards reaction is endothermic then increasing the temperature will increase the amount of product made.

KEY POINT

In a dynamic equilibrium, both the forwards and the backwards reactions are still happening. As they happen at the same rate there is no overall change in the concentrations of the reactants or the products.

Reactions involving gases

OCR A	C7	✓
OCR B	C2, C5	✓
CCEA	C2	✓

If a reaction involves gases then the pressure may affect the **yield** of the reaction.

First, count the number of gas molecules on the left-hand side and the right-hand side of the equation.

reactants → products
fewer gas molecules → more gas molecules

Increasing the pressure decreases the yield of the product.

reactants → products
more gas molecules → fewer gas molecules

Increasing the pressure increases the yield of the product.

Contact process

OCR B	C5	✓
CCEA	C2	✓
WJEC	C3	✓

The contact process is used in the manufacture of sulfuric acid, H_2SO_4.

First, sulfur is burned in air to produce sulfur dioxide.

$$S(s) + O_2(g) \rightarrow SO_2(g)$$

Then the sulfur dioxide is reacted with more oxygen to form sulfur trioxide.

$$2SO_2(g) + O_2(g) \rightarrow 2SO_3(g)$$

The forward reaction is exothermic.

Choosing the conditions for the contact process

The vanadium(V) oxide catalyst is used in the contact process because it increases the rate of reaction, which helps to reduce production costs.

A moderate temperature of 450°C is chosen. A higher temperature would give a faster rate of reaction but a lower yield of sulfur trioxide. A lower temperature would give a higher yield of sulfur trioxide but a lower rate of reaction. A moderate temperature gives both a reasonable rate of reaction and a reasonable yield of the product.

A higher pressure would increase the yield of the reaction as well as the rate because it would favour the forwards reaction, which decreases the number of gaseous molecules. However, it is expensive to maintain high pressures and, as the yield is already around 95%, it is not necessary.

Finally, the sulfur trioxide is reacted with sulfuric acid to produce oleum, $H_2S_2O_7$.

$$SO_3 + H_2SO_4 \rightarrow H_2S_2O_7$$

The oleum is then reacted with water to form more sulfuric acid.

$$H_2S_2O_7 + H_2O \rightarrow 2H_2SO_4$$

PROGRESS CHECK

1. What is special about a reversible reaction?
2. What is a closed system?
3. What is a dynamic equilibrium?
4. The contact process is used in the production of sulfuric acid.
   a) Name the catalyst used in the contact process.
   b) Explain why a moderate temperature of 450°C is used in this reaction.

1. It can proceed in either direction.
2. It is where nothing can enter or leave.
3. It is where the rate of forwards and backwards reactions are the same, so there is no change in the overall concentrations of reactants or products.
4. a) Vanadium(V) oxide.
   b) A higher temperature would give a faster rate of reaction but a lower yield of sulfur trioxide. A lower temperature would give a higher yield of sulfur trioxide but a lower rate of reaction. A moderate temperature gives both a reasonable rate of reaction and a reasonable yield of the product.

6.6 The Haber process

LEARNING SUMMARY

After studying this section, you should be able to:

- Write a balanced equation for the reaction between nitrogen and hydrogen to produce ammonia.
- Describe how the optimum conditions for ammonia production are chosen.
- Understand the role of the iron catalyst in keeping costs down.
- Recall the main uses of ammonia.
- Describe the conversion of ammonia into nitric acid.

Making ammonia

AQA	C3	✓
OCR A	C7	✓
OCR B	C2	✓
EDEXCEL	C2, C3	✓
CCEA	C2	✓
WJEC	C3	✓

Ammonia is produced by the **Haber process** and is made from **nitrogen** and **hydrogen**.

KEY POINT

Hydrogen is obtained from natural gas or from the **cracking** of oil fractions. Nitrogen is obtained from the **fractional distillation** of liquid air. This is an example of a **reversible reaction**.

$$N_2(g) + 3H_2(g) \rightleftharpoons 2NH_3(g)$$

Some of the nitrogen and the hydrogen react to form ammonia. At the same time, some of the ammonia breaks down into nitrogen and hydrogen.

On cooling, the ammonia **liquefies** and is removed from the reaction mixture.

Any unreacted nitrogen and hydrogen can be recycled to cut costs. Ammonia is made on a very large scale.

Cost of producing ammonia

OCR A	C7	✓
OCR B	C2	✓
EDEXCEL	C2, C3	✓
CCEA	C2	✓
WJEC	C3	✓

The cost of producing ammonia depends on:

- The cost of the raw materials.
- Energy costs.
- Equipment costs.
- Labour costs – the more automation the lower the wages bill will be.
- How quickly the ammonia is produced.

Choosing the conditions for the Haber process

AQA	C3	✓
OCR A	C7	✓
OCR B	C2	✓
EDEXCEL	C2, C3	✓
CCEA	C2	✓
WJEC	C3	✓

KEY POINT

The industrial conditions are specially chosen. Typical conditions are:

- A high pressure (200 atmospheres).
- A moderate temperature (450°C).
- An iron **catalyst**.

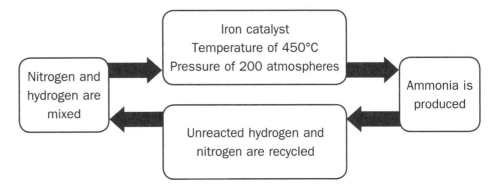

A **high pressure** is used to increase the amount of ammonia produced. In the balanced symbol equation, there are four gas molecules on the left-hand side of the equation (one nitrogen molecule and three hydrogen molecules), but there are only two ammonia molecules on the right-hand side of the equation. Increasing the pressure encourages the forwards reaction, which increases the amount of ammonia produced because there are fewer gas molecules on the right-hand side of the equation. Ideally, the highest possible pressures should be used. However, in practice, it is too expensive to build a plant that can withstand pressures greater than 200 atmospheres.

The reaction between nitrogen and hydrogen to produce ammonia is **exothermic**. A low temperature would increase the **yield** of ammonia produced at equilibrium. It would, however, also make the rate of the reaction very slow. A higher temperature would give a much faster rate of reaction. The yield of ammonia at **equilibrium**, however, would be much lower. In practice, a compromise temperature of 450°C is used. This gives a reasonable yield of ammonia reasonably quickly.

To get a top grade, you need to explain the conditions used in the Haber process. In the Haber process it is not enough just to state that compromise conditions are used. You should explain why it is a compromise in terms of the rate of reaction and the yield of ammonia.

An iron catalyst is used to increase the rate of reaction. This helps to reduce the costs of making ammonia. Catalysts are not used up during the reaction so they can be used many times. Different catalysts work for different reactions but **transition metals** and their **compounds** are often good catalysts.

Making fertilisers

OCR A	C7	✓
OCR B	C2	✓
EDEXCEL	C3	✓
CCEA	C2	✓

Fertilisers replace the essential elements used by plants as they grow, so the manufacture of ammonia is important for the world's food production. Many fertilisers contain nitrogen, which is needed for plant growth. Popular artificial fertilisers include ammonium nitrate, ammonium phosphate and ammonium sulfate.

Plants absorb the chemicals in these fertilisers through their roots, so fertilisers must be soluble in water. Phosphorus and potassium are also needed for plants to grow well.

Making nitric acid

| OCR B | C2 | ✓ |

Ammonia can be oxidised to produce nitric acid. Ammonia gas reacts with oxygen in the air over a platinum catalyst.

$$4NH_3 + 5O_2 \rightarrow 4NO + 6H_2O$$

The nitrogen oxide is cooled and then reacted with water and more oxygen to form nitric acid.

$$4NO + 3O_2 + 2H_2O \rightarrow 4HNO_3$$

Ammonium nitrate

Nitric acid can be neutralised with ammonia to make ammonium nitrate.

ammonia + nitric acid → ammonium nitrate

Make sure you can apply this idea to the production of ammonium phosphate, ammonium sulfate and potassium nitrate

Fixing nitrogen

| OCR A | C7 | ✓ |

Some living organisms can **fix** (that is, hold on to) nitrogen from the air at room temperature and pressure by using **enzymes**. Scientists have found that they can alter nitrogen **fixation levels** by using different catalysts. Scientists are now interested in developing new, more efficient catalysts that behave like the enzymes found in living organisms. Some ammonia is used to produce cleaning fluids.

> **PROGRESS CHECK**
>
> 1 What does the Haber process produce?
> 2 From where are the hydrogen and nitrogen obtained?
> 3 Why could this reaction be described as reversible?
> 4 Explain how ammonia can be made into ammonium nitrate. Include symbol equations to sum up each step in the production of this fertiliser.
>
> 1. Ammonia.
> 2. Hydrogen is obtained from natural gas or the cracking of oil fractions. Nitrogen is obtained from the fractional distillation of liquid air.
> 3. The reaction can go forwards or backwards.
> 4. React the ammonia with oxygen in the air over a platinum catalyst.
> $4NH_3 + 5O_2 \rightarrow 4NO + 6H_2O$
> Allow the nitrogen oxide to cool, and then react it with water and more oxygen to form nitric acid.
> $4NO + 3O_2 + 2H_2O \rightarrow 4HNO_3$
> Then react the nitric acid with more ammonia to form ammonium nitrate.
> $HNO_3 + NH_3 \rightarrow NH_4NO_3$

6.7 Exothermic and endothermic reactions

LEARNING SUMMARY

After studying this section, you should be able to:

- Understand the terms 'exothermic' and 'endothermic', applied to chemical reactions.
- Recall that bond breaking is always endothermic and bond making exothermic.
- Calculate energy changes from the bond energies of bonds broken and made.
- Interpret energy level diagrams for exothermic and endothermic reactions.
- Understand how the activation energy is affected by a catalyst.

Energy changes and chemical reactions

AQA	C2, C3 ✓
OCR A	C6, C7 ✓
OCR B	C3 ✓
EDEXCEL	C2 ✓
WJEC	C2, C3 ✓
CCEA	C2 ✓

During chemical reactions atoms are rearranged as old **bonds** are broken and new bonds are made.

> **KEY POINT**
>
> **Energy** is required to break bonds and is released when new bonds are formed.

If, overall, energy is given to the surroundings, the reaction is described as **exothermic**. If, overall, energy is taken from the surroundings, the reaction is described as **endothermic**.

To work out whether a reaction is endothermic or exothermic, scientists take the temperature of the chemicals before the reaction and then after the reaction. If the temperature has increased the reaction is exothermic; if the temperature has decreased the reaction is endothermic.

Burning methane is an example of an **exothermic reaction**. Rusting, explosions and neutralisation reactions are also exothermic. Self-heating cans and hand warmers make use of exothermic reactions.

The **thermal decomposition** of limestone is an example of an **endothermic reaction**. Photosynthesis and dissolving ammonium nitrate in water are also endothermic reactions. Some sports injury packs make use of endothermic reactions to cool wounds.

Bond energy calculations

OCR A	C7	✓
EDEXCEL	C2	✓
WJEC	C2	✓

Each chemical bond has a specific **bond energy**. This is the amount of energy that must be taken in to break 1 mole of bonds.

Bond	Bond energy (kJ mol^{-1})
C–H	413
O=O	496
C=O	743
O–H	463
C–O	358

Example: Burning the fuel methane, CH_4.

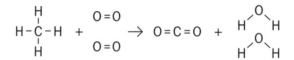

Energy taken in to break the bonds:

- 4 moles of C–H = 4 × 413 = 1652 kJ mol^{-1}
- 2 moles of O=O = 2 × 496 = 992 kJ mol^{-1}
- Total = 1652 + 992 = 2644 kJ mol^{-1}

Energy taken in has a positive sign (endothermic).

Energy given out when forming bonds:

- 2 moles of C=O = 2 × 743 = 1486 kJ mol^{-1}
- 4 moles of O–H = 4 × 463 = 1852 kJ mol^{-1}
- Total = 1486 + 1852 = 3338 kJ mol^{-1}

Energy given out has a negative sign (exothermic).

Difference in energy between energy given out and the energy taken in:

= +2644 kJ mol^{-1} – 3338 kJ mol^{-1}

= –694 kJ mol^{-1}

This reaction gives out more energy than it takes in so it is exothermic. The burning of fuels is always exothermic.

Energy level diagrams

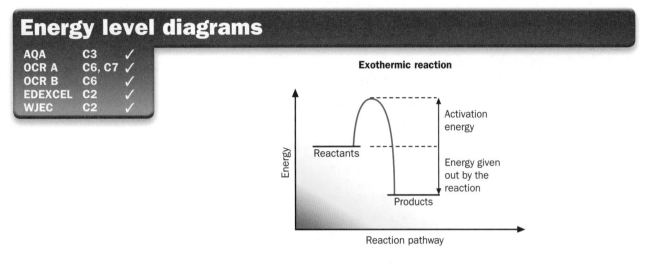

AQA	C3	✓
OCR A	C6, C7	✓
OCR B	C6	✓
EDEXCEL	C2	✓
WJEC	C2	✓

Exothermic reaction

In an exothermic reaction, the products have less energy than the reactants. The difference in energy between the products and the reactants is the amount of energy given out by the reaction.

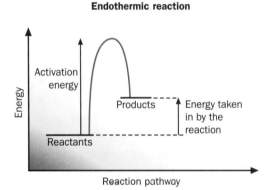

Endothermic reaction

In an endothermic reaction, the products have more energy than the reactants. The difference in energy between the products and the reactants is the amount of energy taken in by the reaction.

Catalysed exothermic reaction

| AQA | C3 | ✓ |
| OCR A | C7 | ✓ |

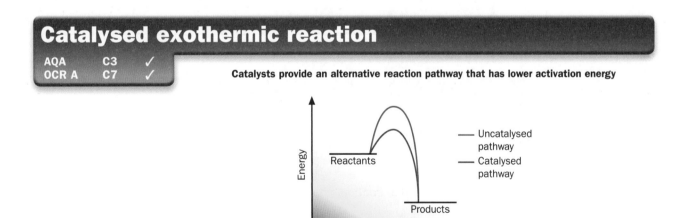

Catalysts provide an alternative reaction pathway that has lower activation energy

More reactant particles will have the lower activation energy, so catalysed reactions happen faster. Catalysts increase the rate of reaction but are not used up during the reaction.

Activation energy

AQA	C3	✓
OCR A	C7	✓
WJEC	C2	✓
CCEA	C2	✓

KEY POINT

The **activation energy** is the minimum amount of energy needed to get the **reaction** started. This energy is needed to break the bonds in the reactants. Catalysts provide an alternative reaction pathway that has lower activation energy.

It is very important that scientists continue to develop better **catalysts** that lower activation energies. By using a catalyst, it is possible to increase the rate of reaction. This means lower temperatures and pressures can be used, which has economic benefits, because it costs less, and environmental benefits, as high temperatures and pressures are often obtained by using electricity generated at power stations that burn fossil fuels. If less fossil fuel is being burned then less carbon dioxide is being released into the atmosphere. Using better catalysts also helps to preserve raw materials.

PROGRESS CHECK

1. The temperature increases during a chemical reaction. What sort of reaction has taken place?
2. How do you know that burning coal is an exothermic reaction?
3. When hydrochloric acid neutralises sodium hydroxide the temperature increases. Is this an exothermic reaction or an endothermic reaction?
4. Sketch an energy level diagram for the combustion of methane.

4. The vertical axis should be labelled 'energy' and the horizontal axis should be labelled 'time' or 'reaction pathway'. The reactants should be labelled as methane and oxygen and should be higher than the products, which should be labelled as carbon dioxide and water. The energy change and the activation energy should also be marked.
3. Exothermic.
2. It releases lots of energy.
1. Exothermic.

6.8 Explaining energy changes

LEARNING SUMMARY

After studying this section, you should be able to:
- Describe how the energy change of a reaction can be measured using calorimetry.
- Recall that the temperature increase in a volume of water can be converted to an energy charge.
- Understand the term 'specific heat capacity' and recall how this is used in the calculation.
- Recognise that heat energy produced can be in kJ/mol, kJ/g or calories/g.
- Recall that burning fuels, displacement reactions and neutralisation reactions are usually exothermic.

Calorimetry

| AQA | C3 | ✓ |
| OCR B | C3 | ✓ |

In **exothermic** reactions, more energy is given out when new bonds are formed than when the bonds were broken. In **endothermic** reactions, more energy is taken in to break bonds than is released when new bonds are formed.

Scientists use **calorimetry** to compare the amount of energy released when fuels and foods are burned. A fixed amount of water is placed into a boiling tube and its temperature is taken using a thermometer.

Calorimetry

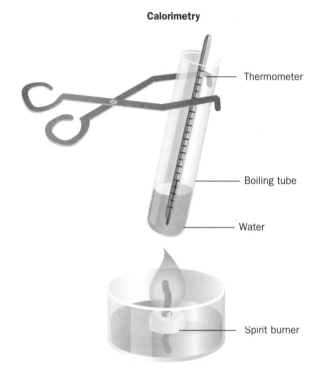

- Thermometer
- Boiling tube
- Water
- Spirit burner

Remember, combustion reactions are exothermic. Try making a list of all the other exothermic reactions you have learned about.

The sample is then burned under the boiling tube containing the water, and the water is gradually warmed up. The temperature of the water is taken at the end of the experiment.

To compare the energy transferred when liquid fuels are burned, place the fuel in a **spirit burner**. Find the mass of the spirit burner and the fuel. Use the spirit burner to heat the water, then find the new mass of the remaining fuel and the spirit burner. The amount of fuel used is the difference between the mass at the start and at the end.

The chemical energy that had been stored in the sample is released as thermal energy when the sample is burned. The greater the change in temperature of the water the more energy was stored in the fuel.

Specific heat capacity

| AQA | C3 | ✓ |

> **KEY POINT**
>
> **Energy change = mass × specific heat capacity × change in temperature**

Specific heat capacity (SHC) is the amount of energy needed to increase the temperature of 1 g of the substance by 1°C.

The SHC of water is 4.2 J/g/°C.

$1 cm^3$ of water has a mass of 1 g.

Example: A 2 g sample of food made the temperature of $5 cm^3$ of water increase by 6°C.

Energy change = mass × specific heat capacity × change in temperature
$$= 5 g × 4.2 J/g/°C × 6°C$$
$$= 126 J$$

Although energy is usually measured in joules other units, such as kilojoules or calories, can be used.

- 1000 joules = 1 kilojoule
- 1 calorie = 4.2 joules

To be able to compare the energy content of different samples, energy values are normally given for the same amount of substance: joules per gram, kilojoules per gram or calories per gram.

The energy values for example 1 are given below using different units:

Joules per gram $\quad = \dfrac{125.4 \text{ J}}{2 \text{ g}} = \dfrac{62.7 \text{ J}}{\text{g}}$

kilojoules per gram $\quad = \dfrac{125.4 \text{ J}}{1000 \text{ g}} = 0.1254 \text{ kJ}$

$\dfrac{0.1254 \text{ kJ}}{2 \text{ g}} = 0.0627 \text{ kJ/g}$

Calories per gram $\quad = \dfrac{125.4 \text{ calories}}{4.2 \text{ calories}} = 29.9 \text{ calories}$

$\dfrac{29.9 \text{ calories}}{2 \text{ g}} = 14.9 \text{ calories per gram}$

In these equations, the mass is the mass of the water, not the mass of the fuel or the chemicals used.

A displacement reaction

AQA	C3	✓
OCR B	C3	✓
EDEXCEL	C2	✓

Calorimetry experiments can be used to work out the energy released by chemical reactions in solution. In the example below, a more reactive metal, iron, displaces a less reactive metal, copper from a solution of copper sulfate.

Measuring the temperature change of a displacement reaction

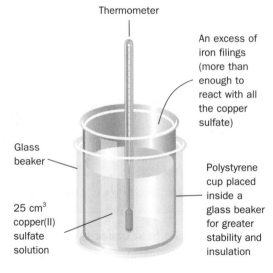

Thermometer

An excess of iron filings (more than enough to react with all the copper sulfate)

Glass beaker

Polystyrene cup placed inside a glass beaker for greater stability and insulation

$25 cm^3$ copper(II) sulfate solution

Temperature at the start of the reaction.	15°C
Temperature at the end of the reaction.	33°C
Change in temperature.	18°C

The specific heat capacity of copper(II) sulfate solution = 4.2 J/g/°C.

Calculating the energy change

AQA	C3	✓
OCR B	C3	✓

Calorimetry can also be used to measure the energy change when solids **dissolve** in water and in **neutralisation** reactions.

The reaction above is carried out inside an insulated container, such as a polystyrene cup. The temperature of the solution is taken at the start and end of the experiment to work out the change in temperature. As 1 cm^3 of solution is assumed to have a mass of 1 g, a mass of 25 g is used for the mass of the solution.

Energy change = mass × specific heat capacity × change in temperature
= 25 g × 4.2 J/g/°C × 18°C
= 1890 J or 1.890 kJ

PROGRESS CHECK

1. What happens in chemical reactions?
2. Name the piece of apparatus used to measure temperature.
3. Why must the temperature of the water be recorded at the beginning and at the end of the experiment?
4. What sort of energy is stored in food and fuels?
5. What sort of energy is released when food and fuels are burned?
6. A sample of sodium hydroxide pellets are dissolved in 25.0 g water. The initial temperature of the water was 18°C and the final temperature was 35°C. The specific heat capacity of distilled water = 4.2 J/g/°C.
    a) What sort of material should the container for this reaction be made from?
    b) How much energy is given out in this process? Give your answer in kilojoules to 3 significant figures.

1. Bonds are broken and new bonds are formed.
2. A thermometer.
3. To work out the temperature change.
4. Chemical energy.
5. Thermal energy.
6. a) It should be made from an insulator such as polystyrene.
   b) Energy change = mass × specific heat capacity × change in temperature
   = 25 g × 4.2 J/g/°C × 17°C
   = 1785 J
   = 1.785 kJ

Sample GCSE questions

1 The graph, below, follows the volume of carbon dioxide released by the reaction between excess calcium carbonate, in the form of marble chips, and hydrochloric acid solution over time.

$$CaCO_3(s) + 2HCl(aq) \rightarrow CaCl_2(aq) + CO_2(g) + H_2O(l)$$

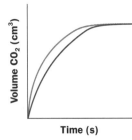

(a) **(i)** What feature of the graph shows the rate of the reaction? **[1]**

The gradient of this type of graph shows the rate of reaction.

(ii) Describe what happens to the rate of this reaction over the period of time shown. **[2]**

The rate is high at the start, but gradually decreases to zero.

← Remember you are commenting on the gradient, not the volume of CO_2.

(iii) Use the collision theory to explain the change in rate you have described. **[2]**

As the acid reacts, the number of particles of acid falls, meaning that collisions between acid particles and the marble become fewer.

(b) **(i)** Draw a second line on the graph, showing what you would expect if the same volume of acid had been diluted with an equal volume of water before adding it to the marble chips. **[2]**

← The second line should be less steep at the start, but it should follow the same shape of curve and end up at exactly the same volume of CO_2.

(ii) Explain why the second line, that you have added, is different to the first. **[2]**

It is less steep at the start because there is a lower concentration of acid. Fewer particles of acid (per cm^3) will result in fewer collisions.

(iii) Comment on the total volume of CO_2 produced in both experiments. **[2]**

Although the acid is diluted in the second experiment, there is still the same amount of acid to react, so the volume of CO_2 produced will be the same.

Sample GCSE questions

2 Hydrogen reacts with oxygen to make water. In this reaction, covalent bonds are broken and made, leading to an energy change.

$$2H_2(g) + O_2(g) \rightarrow 2H_2O(l)$$

Bond energies: H-H 436kJ/mol
O=O 498kJ/mol
H-O 464kJ/mol

(a) **(i)** Use the bond energy data to calculate the energy change for the reaction between hydrogen and oxygen. **[3]**

bonds broken   bonds made
2×436 4×464
$+1 \times 498$ 1856

Total 1370

$1370 - 1856 = -486kJ/mol$

Set out a 'balance sheet'.

Remember that you subtract the energy of the bonds made from the energy of the bonds broken to get the total energy change.

(ii) Is the reaction exothermic or endothermic? Explain how you can tell.

Exothermic, because there is a negative value for total energy change. **[2]**

(b) **(i)** A mixture of hydrogen gas with oxygen gas needs a spark to ignite it. Explain why a spark is needed at the start of the reaction. **[2]**

The spark provides the activation energy, which is needed to break bonds at the start of the reaction.

(ii) On the energy profile diagram, below, draw a line between the reactants and products that shows the need for a spark to ignite the mixture. **[2]**

Activation energy for an exothermic reaction is shown as a 'hump', between the higher energy of the reactants and the energy of the products. For the second mark, the height of the hump should be marked and labelled, E_A or 'activation energy'.

hydrogen + oxygen

E_A

Energy

water

Reaction

(iii) Describe how the presence of a catalyst would alter the energy profile diagram. **[1]**

The activation energy would be lower.

Exam practice questions

① The relative atomic masses of calcium, carbon and oxygen are 40, 12 and 16, respectively.

(a) What is the relative formula mass of calcium carbonate, $CaCO_3$? [1]

....

(b) How many moles is 25 g of calcium carbonate? [1]

....

(c) What is the relative formula mass of calcium oxide, CaO? [1]

....

(d) What mass is lost when 100 g of calcium carbonate turns into calcium oxide? Explain this loss in mass. [2]

....

....

② Magnesium metal burns in oxygen according to the equation:

$2Mg(s) + O_2(g) \rightarrow 2MgO(s)$

(a) What is the mass, in grams, of two moles of magnesium (relative atomic mass 24)? [1]

....

(b) What mass of oxygen (relative atomic mass 16) would this combine with? [1]

....

(c) What mass of magnesium oxide would be produced? [1]

....

(d) Calculate the mass of magnesium oxide produced by burning 6 g of magnesium. [2]

....

....

③ 28 g of iron (relative atomic mass 56) reacts completely with 35.5 g of chlorine gas (relative atomic mass of chlorine is 35.5).

(a) What is the formula of the iron chloride that is produced? [2]

....

....

(b) What volume, in dm^3 would 35.5 g of chlorine (Cl_2) occupy at room temperature and pressure? [1]

....

(c) How many chlorine atoms are in 0.5 moles of chlorine, (Cl_2)? [1]

....

Exam practice questions

(d) What mass of iron chloride could be produced from 0.5 moles of chlorine (Cl_2)? **[1]**

....

4 Look at the data table. It shows how temperature and pressure affect the yield (%) of the product in an industrial process.

Pressure (atmospheres)	Temperature (°C)			
	250	350	450	550
50	60%	30%	11%	4%
100	67%	34%	16%	7%
200	73%	50%	29%	14%

(a) What temperature gives the lowest yield? **[1]**

....

(b) What is the yield at 100 atmospheres pressure and a temperature of 350°C? **[1]**

....

(c) What happens to the yield as the temperature is decreased? **[1]**

....

5 In the contact process, sulfur dioxide reacts with oxygen to make sulfur trioxide, which is then used to make sulfuric acid:

$$2SO_2(g) + O_2(g) \rightleftharpoons 2SO_3(g)$$

(a) What is meant by the symbol $\rightleftharpoons$ in this reaction? **[1]**

....

(b) What do you understand by the term 'dynamic equilibrium'? **[2]**

....

....

(c) To favour the production of SO_3, should a high or a low pressure be used? **[1]**

....

(d) If the forward reaction is exothermic, should a high or low temperature be used? **[1]**

....

6 In the Haber process, nitrogen and hydrogen react to make ammonia:

$$N_2(g) + 3H_2(g) \rightleftharpoons 2NH_3(g)$$

(a) What is the source of the nitrogen used in the Haber process? **[1]**

....

(b) Why is a catalyst used? **[1]**

....

Exam practice questions

(c) What are the optimum conditions (temperature and pressure) for the process? **[2]**

....

....

(d) How is the ammonia separated from the reaction mixture? **[1]**

....

7 **(a)** Explain what must happen to reactant particles for a reaction to take place. **[2]**

....

....

(b) Look at the graph below. The curve from the original reaction is labelled.

Select the curve on this graph that represents the curve showing the same reaction but using:

(i) a lower original temperature. **[1]**

....

(ii) half the original amount of reactants. **[1]**

....

(iii) Describe how you would use the graph to compare the speed of the original
reaction with the speed of reaction B. **[2]**

....

....

(c) Explain why some collisions do not result in a successful reaction. **[2]**

....

....

8 A student dissolves 10.0 g of a salt in 100 cm^3 of water, in an insulated polystyrene cup. The
temperature of the water falls by 12°C. The specific heat capacity of water is 4.18 J/g/°C.

(a) Is the dissolving of this salt exothermic or endothermic? **[1]**

....

Exam practice questions

(b) Use the data given to calculate the heat energy change, in Joules, to dissolve 10 g of the salt. **[2]**

....

....

(c) How would the student measure the temperature change as the salt dissolved? **[1]**

....

(d) Why is important to use an insulated polystyrene cup in the experiment? **[1]**

....

9 Calculate how many moles are present in the following:

(a) 14.0 g of iron (relative atomic mass 56) **[1]**

....

(b) 25 cm^3 of a sodium hydroxide solution with concentration 2.0 mol/dm^3 **[1]**

....

(c) 8.0 dm^3 of oxygen at room temperature and pressure **[1]**

....

(d) 1.0 dm^3 of water (density 1 g/cm^3), given relative atomic masses H: 1 and O: 16 **[2]**

....

....

10 Using acids in chemical reactions and in industrial processes may be dangerous. The potential hazard depends on the acid strength and its concentration.

Explain the difference between the strength of an acid and its concentration, making it clear how each affects how hazardous it is to use the acid.

The quality of written communication will be assessed in your answer to this question. **[6]**

....

....

....

....

....

....

....

....

Answers

Note: For questions involving QWC, marks will be awarded if:
- All information in answer is relevant, clear, organised and presented in a structured and coherent format.
- Specialist terms are used appropriately.
- There are few, if any, errors in grammar, punctuation and spelling.

Chapter 1

1. (a) 10
   (b) 20
   (c) (2, 8)
   (d) Period 2; Group 8
2. (a) 3
   (b) 5
   (c) It has lost; two electrons
   (d) 2−
3. (a) The transition or d-block
   (b) Metals
4. (a) $Mg(s) + Cl_2(g) \rightarrow MgCl_2(s)$
   (b) $4Fe(s) + 3O_2(g) \rightarrow 2Fe_2O_3(s)$
5. (a) Gas
   (b) A molecule
   (c) $3H_2$ and $2NH_3$
   (d) Water or H_2O
6. (a) 8
   (b) Cl^-
   (c) 2
   (d) 2 electrons in overlap region; 6 other electrons in Cl shell

7. (a) Diamond has a giant molecular structure; Each of the carbon atoms forms four covalent bonds with other carbon atoms, making it a very hard substance; It has a very high melting point and boiling point but it is unable to conduct electricity because there are no available electrons
   (b) In graphite the carbon atoms are only covalently bonded to three further carbon atoms, leaving the fourth electron from each atom to move freely about the structure; This allows graphite to conduct electricity; The atoms within the structure of graphite are arranged in layers that are able to slide past each other, which allows graphite to be used in pencils and as a lubricant
8. (a) They increase
   (b) It decreases
   (c) As you go down the group there are more electron shells; which shield the nucleus so it cannot attract electron
9. (a) The materials for the new drug could be rare or may require expensive extraction from plants.
   (b) You can make a product quickly on demand; You can make a product on a small scale; The equipment can be used to make a variety of products
10. (See QWC guidance on page 206.)
    Magnesium oxide would be solid at room temperature.
    Magnesium oxide would have a high melting point.
    Magnesium oxide would have a high boiling point.
    Because the attraction between magnesium ions and oxide ions is very strong.
    Ionic bonds are not easily broken.
    Magnesium oxide would conduct electricity when molten.
    Because melting frees the ions, allowing them to move.

Chapter 2

1. (a) Photosynthesis
   (b) Oxygen
   (c) There will be fewer green plants; so less photosynthesis
2. (a) Fractional distillation
   (b) Different boiling points
   (c) Nitrogen and oxygen
3. (a) Nitrogen
   (b) 21%
   (c) Any suitable answer e.g. carbon dioxide
4. (a) Does not decompose naturally
   (b) Toxic gases may be released into the atmosphere
   (c) Re-use or recycle
5. CFCs break down and release chlorine atoms (radicals); which destroy ozone molecules and make the ozone thinner
6. David is correct, except for one value (8 km); Improvements could be made by: measuring more than one gas, monitoring over a longer time period, calculating or basing claims on average levels (any two)
7. There is less photosynthesis; Less carbon dioxide removed from air; Less oxygen made; The burning of the trees puts carbon dioxide into the air; Removes oxygen
8. (a) Helium does not burn; Hydrogen burns explosively
   (b) Argon is too dense
9. (a) It produces irreversible changes in food
   (b) They are denatured
   (c) Starch grains swell; bursting the cell walls
10. (a) $N_2(g) + 2CO_2(g)$
    (b) They cause acid rain
    (c) Carbon dioxide is now regarded as a pollutant
11. The more dense oceanic plate is pushed under the continental plate; Down into the mantle where it melts; The result is a mountain range and possibly volcanoes
12. (See QWC guidance on page 206.)
    Reduction in atmospheric carbon dioxide.
    Reduction in the 'greenhouse effect'.
    Atmospheric temperature lowered.
    Water vapour (steam) condensed to form liquid.
    Ammonia turned into nitrogen by bacteria.
    Oxygen produced by green plants.
    Oxygen needed by all living things for respiration.

Chapter 3

1. (a) Ethanol
   (b) Ethene
   (c) Ethene
   (d) Ethanol
2. (a) C_4H_{10}
   (b) Butane is saturated
   (c) Alkanes
   (d) Add bromine solution; butene will decolourise it
3. (a) Esters
   (b) Sodium hydroxide
   (c) The salt; of a fatty acid
   (d) Turn it into biodiesel, use it to make margarine etc.
4. (a) The ethene molecules join together to form chains
   (b) $-(-C_2H_4-)-_n$
   (c) It softens; on heating
   (d) It has greater crystallinity
5. (a) C_2H_5OH
   (b) Sugar

Answers

(c) $C_6H_{12}O_6 \rightarrow 2C_2H_5OH + 2CO_2$ (1 mark for formulae, 1 mark for balancing)

(d) As it is used, more can be produced at almost the same rate

6 (a) -O-H

(b) Forces between molecules are stronger in propanol

(c) propanol + oxygen $\rightarrow$ carbon dioxide + water

(d) It is a solvent

7 Petrol

8 (a) So that the nail varnish does not wash off when hands are washed

(b) Bonds between water molecules are stronger; than bonds between water and nail varnish molecules

(c) The solvent is evaporating

(d) So that the nail varnish dries quickly

9 (a) Isomers have the same molecular formula; but different structures

(b) Butane

(c) C_4H_{10}

(d) A structural formula or displayed formula

10 (a) The fractions can be separated and collected because hydrocarbons; boil at different temperatures

(b) Any one from: Breaking up large hydrocarbon molecules into small hydrocarbon molecules; To match supply and demand; To make more petrol; To make ethane

(c) Small molecules have fewer forces of attraction between molecules than large molecules; Less energy is needed to separate them

11 (a) Hydrogenation increases the melting point makes it solid

(b) High temperature, pressure and a catalyst

(c) The molecules contain C=C double bonds

(d) Add bromine solution; unsaturation is shown by loss of colour

12 (a) Chloroethene or 'vinyl chloride'

(b) Addition polymerisation

(c) PVC is lighter; and will not rust

(d) Plasticisers

13 (See QWC guidance on page 206.)

Sugar is an inexpensive raw material.
Ethene comes from cracking hydrocarbons.
High temperature and pressure increase cost.
Fermentation happens at low temperatures.
Fermentation is catalysed by yeast enzymes.
Fermentation is a batch process.
Hydration of ethene is a continuous process.
Atom economy of hydrating ethane is 100%.
Ethanol produced by fermentation has to be distilled to separate it.

Chapter 4

1 (a) Delocalised means not part of one particular atom

(b) Electrostatic attraction; between positive ions and electrons

(c) Electrical conductivity

2 (a) Hydrogen

(b) Sodium hydroxide

(c) $2Na + 2H_2O \rightarrow 2NaOH + H_2$ (1 mark for formulae, 1 mark for balancing)

3 (a) An ore contains enough of a metal; to make extraction economically viable

(b) Carbon

(c) Silicon dioxide

4 Aluminium can only be extracted by electrolysis; Aluminium oxide cannot be reduced by carbon because carbon is less reactive than aluminium; Iron is extracted by heating the iron oxide with carbon; because carbon is more reactive than iron

5 (a) Any two from: It is stronger; It is easier to shape; It is more flexible

(b) Tin

(c) Any two from: It is hard; It is strong; It has a low melting point; It is gas proof.

6 (a) Aluminium metal

(b) Oxygen

(c) Cryolite; to reduce its melting point

(d) A lot of electricity is used to extract the aluminium

7 (a) Steel

(b) Aluminium has a lower density so panels are lighter

(c) Aluminium is more expensive than steel

(d) Aluminium does not rust; so scrap aluminium is much purer than scrap steel

8 (a) The transition, or d-block

(b) It has an attractive colour; It does not oxidise/tarnish in air (allow it is soft and easy to shape)

(c) Copper

(d) The Carat scale

9 (a) Any suitable answer that gives the idea of clean emissions, e.g. It does not produce carbon dioxide; It does not cause global warming; It produces only water. Or: It is renewable.

(b) Fuel cells contain poisonous catalysts that must be removed before it is disposed of; Burning fossil fuels produces the electricity used in fuel cells to decompose water to form hydrogen and water.

10 (a) The cation (metal ion) present in a salt

(b) Sodium ions are present

(c) Both give a green flame colour

(d) The wire must be free from any salts previously tested; which might give false flame colours

11 (a) An acidified solution of silver nitrate

(b) A precipitate is formed

(c) Chloride gives a white precipitate; bromide gives a cream precipitate

(d) $Ag^+(aq) + Cl^-(aq) \rightarrow AgCl(s)$

12 (a) Nickel and titanium

(b) It bends

(c) If they are accidentally bent, they can easily be repaired

13 (See QWC guidance on page 206.)

Petrol and diesel engines use non-renewable fossil fuels.
Fuel cells use hydrogen and oxygen instead of fossil fuels.
Hydrogen and oxygen can be obtained from water.
The fuel cell produces only water as a waste product.
Burning petrol or diesel produces carbon dioxide.
Carbon dioxide contributes to the greenhouse effect and/or global warming.
Fuel cells take up less space than petrol or diesel engines.
Fuel cells are more efficient than petrol or diesel engines.

Answers

Chapter 5

1 (a) Hydrochloric acid
   (b) H^+ (or H_3O^+)
   (c) Hydrochloric acid
   (d) Ethanoic acid is weaker; and will not react as much with metals inside the kettle
2 (a) Hydrogen
   (b) The pH increases
   (c) Magnesium sulfate
   (d) Any two from: Magnesium oxide, magnesium hydroxide or magnesium carbonate
3 (a) Calcium carbonate
   (b) It is heated; with clay
   (c) At least one point from environmental, economic and social, plus any additional point, from:
       Environmental: The effect on native animal habitats / landscape; Noise and air pollution; Additional traffic
       Economic: Costs involved in quarrying and processing; Effect on local businesses
       Social: Availability of workforce; How the quarry can be used afterwards
4 (a) By filtration
   (b) Evaporating the water
   (c) Copper(II) carbonate + sulfuric acid → copper(II) sulfate + water (1 mark for reactants, 1 mark for products)
   (d) The reaction is exothermic
5 (a) Sodium chloride
   (b) Hydrogen and chlorine
   (c) Sodium hydroxide
   (d) So they do not react with hydrogen, chlorine or sodium hydroxide
6 (a) The sodium hydroxide solution
   (b) An indicator
   (c) A burette
   (d) 0.2 mol/dm^3 (1 mark for showing working)
7 (a) Farmers apply nitrates to fields; which are washed into rivers by rainwater
   (b) Nitrates are all soluble in water
   (c) To kill bacteria
   (d) By limiting the amount applied to the fields
8 (a) Calcium hydrogencarbonate
   (b) Limescale, deposited when water is heated; and scum, which forms when hardness reacts with soap
   (c) Minerals in hard water react with the soap; Some of the soap becomes insoluble as it is used up in the reaction; It is hard to form lather because scum is produced
   (d) It exchanges calcium ions for sodium ions
9 (a) H^+ (or H_3O^+)
   (b) OH^-
   (c) $H^+(aq) + OH^-(aq) \rightarrow H_2O(l)$
   (d) The pH increases
10 (a) Marble is harder than limestone
   (b) Calcium oxide and carbon dioxide
   (c) Limewater
11 (a) Sodium hydrogencarbonate
   (b) Thermal decomposition
   (c) Bubbles of carbon dioxide; are trapped in the cake mixture
   (d) $2NaHCO_3$ is the only change
12 (a) The indicator changes colour; to show when neutralisation is complete
   (b) Yellow
   (c) Because it gradually changes through a range of colours
13 (See QWC guidance on page 206.)
   Salts can be removed by distilling the water.
   Distribution needs a lot of energy.
   Fuel is burned to provide energy for distillation.
   The water needs to be heated to >100°C to evaporate it.
   The water vapour need to be allowed to cool.
   The water vapour would condense back to liquid water.
   The fuel needed would cost a lot of money.
   The water produced would cost too much.

Chapter 6

1 (a) 100
   (b) 0.25 mol
   (c) 56
   (d) 44 g; 1 mole of carbon dioxide is lost as gas
2 (a) 48 g
   (b) 32 g
   (c) 80 g
   (d) $\dfrac{6}{24} = 0.25$ $0.25 \times 40 = 10$ g
3 (a) $FeCl_3$ (Chlorine is a powerful oxidising agent)
   (b) 12 dm^3
   (c) 1 mol
   (d) 54.7 g
4 (a) 550°C
   (b) 34%
   (c) The yield increases
5 (a) That the reaction is reversible
   (b) The forward and reverse reaction are happening; at the same rate
   (c) High pressure should be used
   (d) Low temperature should be used
6 (a) The air
   (b) To increase the rate of the reaction
   (c) 450°C and 200 atm
   (d) It is cooled and liquefied
7 (a) They must collide; with sufficient energy.
   (b) (i) B
       (ii) C
       (iii) The steeper slope is the faster reaction; Calculate the gradient
   (c) A collision must have enough energy for the particles to react; If they do not have sufficient energy they will not react.
8 (a) The reaction is endothermic
   (b) $100 \times 4.18 \times 12 = 5016$ J (1 mark for calculation and one mark for answer)
   (c) By taking the temperature before and after dissolving
   (d) To reduce heat absorption from the surroundings
9 (a) 0.25 mol
   (b) 0.05 mol
   (c) 0.33 mol
   (d) 1 cm^3 = 1.0 g = 0.055 mol
10 (See QWC guidance on page 206.)
   Acids dissociate in water to produce hydrogen ions.
   The strength of an acid means how fully it ionises in water.
   Strong acids ionise fully.
   Weak acids do not ionise fully.

Answers

Strong acids are not always hazardous but concentrated acids are.

The concentration of an acid means how many moles are dissolved per dm^3.

More concentrated acids react more rapidly than less concentrated acids.

Concentrated acids are more hazardous to use.

Notes

Notes

Notes

Notes

Index

Index

Periodic table

1	2											3	4	5	6	7	0
																	4 **He** helium 2
7 **Li** lithium 3	9 **Be** beryllium 4											11 **B** boron 5	12 **C** carbon 6	14 **N** nitrogen 7	16 **O** oxygen 8	19 **F** fluorine 9	20 **Ne** neon 10
23 **Na** sodium 11	24 **Mg** magnesium 12											27 **Al** aluminium 13	28 **Si** silicon 14	31 **P** phosphorus 15	32 **S** sulfur 16	35.5 **Cl** chlorine 17	40 **Ar** argon 18
39 **K** potassium 19	40 **Ca** calcium 20	45 **Sc** scandium 21	48 **Ti** titanium 22	51 **V** vanadium 23	52 **Cr** chromium 24	55 **Mn** manganese 25	56 **Fe** iron 26	59 **Co** cobalt 27	59 **Ni** nickel 28	63.5 **Cu** copper 29	65 **Zn** zinc 30	70 **Ga** gallium 31	73 **Ge** germanium 32	75 **As** arsenic 33	79 **Se** selenium 34	80 **Br** bromine 35	84 **Kr** krypton 36
85 **Rb** rubidium 37	88 **Sr** strontium 38	89 **Y** yttrium 39	91 **Zr** zirconium 40	93 **Nb** niobium 41	96 **Mo** molybdenum 42	[98] **Tc** technetium 43	101 **Ru** ruthenium 44	103 **Rh** rhodium 45	106 **Pd** palladium 46	108 **Ag** silver 47	112 **Cd** cadmium 48	115 **In** indium 49	119 **Sn** tin 50	122 **Sb** antimony 51	128 **Te** tellurium 52	127 **I** iodine 53	131 **Xe** xenon 54
133 **Cs** caesium 55	137 **Ba** barium 56	139 **La*** lanthanum 57	178 **Hf** hafnium 72	181 **Ta** tantalum 73	184 **W** tungsten 74	186 **Re** rhenium 75	190 **Os** osmium 76	192 **Ir** iridium 77	195 **Pt** platinum 78	197 **Au** gold 79	201 **Hg** mercury 80	204 **Tl** thallium 81	207 **Pb** lead 82	209 **Bi** bismuth 83	[209] **Po** polonium 84	[210] **At** astatine 85	[222] **Rn** radon 86
[223] **Fr** francium 87	[226] **Ra** radium 88	[227] **Ac*** actinium 89	[261] **Rf** rutherfordium 104	[262] **Db** dubnium 105	[266] **Sg** seaborgium 106	[264] **Bh** bohrium 107	[277] **Hs** hassium 108	[268] **Mt** meitnerium 109	[271] **Ds** darmstadtium 110	[272] **Rg** roentgenium 111							

Elements with atomic numbers 112–116 have been reported but not fully authenticated

*The Lanthanides (atomic numbers 58–71) and the Actinides (atomic numbers 90–103) have been omitted.

Cu and **Cl** have not been rounded to the nearest whole number.